NATIONAL GEOGRAPHIC

READING EXPEDITIONS®

SCIENCE

Physical Science

TEACHER'S GUIDE & ASSESSMENTS

Lesson Notes

Activity Masters

Teacher Resources

Copyright © 2004 National Geographic Society

All rights reserved. Reproduction of the whole or any part of the contents without written permission from the publisher is prohibited. National Geographic, National Geographic School Publishing, and the Yellow Border are registered trademarks of the National Geographic Society.

The purchasing educational institution and its staff are permitted to make copies of the pages marked as activity master pages. These pages may be photocopied for non-commercial classroom use only.

Published by the National Geographic Society, Washington, D.C. 20036

ISBN: 0-7922-4862-7
Product # 42052

Produced through the worldwide resources of the National Geographic Society, John M. Fahey, Jr., President and Chief Executive Officer; Gilbert M. Grosvenor, Chairman of the Board; Nina D. Hoffman, Executive Vice President and President, Books and Education Publishing Group.

PREPARED BY NATIONAL GEOGRAPHIC SCHOOL PUBLISHING
Ericka Markman, Senior Vice President and President, Children's Books and Education Publishing Group; Steve Mico, Vice President, Editorial Director; Rosemary Baker, Executive Editor; Barbara Seeber, Editorial Manager; Jim Hiscott, Design Manager; Kristin Hanneman, Illustrations Manager; Matt Wascavage, Manager of Publishing Services; Sean Philpotts, Production Manager; Jane Ponton, Production Artist.

Manufacturing and Quality Control
Christopher A. Liedel, Chief Financial Officer; Phillip L. Schlosser, Director; Clifton M. Brown, Manager

Editorial Services: Navta Associates, The Mazer Corporation, Creative Services Associates, Inc.

Writers: Leslie Morrison and Erin Cleary
Editor: Amy Sarver
Teacher's Guide Design: Steven Curtis Design, Inc.

Picture Credits for the Teacher's Guide:
Cover: background, PhotoDisc®; photos (top to bottom): Digital Stock (3); book covers, top row (left to right): © Roger Allyn Lee/SuperStock; © Streichan/Zefa; © Roger Allyn Lee/Superstock, Inc.; © Orion Press/Black Sheep Stock Photography; bottom row (left to right): © David Parker/IMI/Univ. of Birmingham High, TC Consortium/Science Photo Library; © Roger Allyn Lee/SuperStock; Mitchell Funk/The Image Bank; ©Boden/Ledingham/Masterfile; © Bachman/Photo Network/PictureQuest; page 1: Digital Stock.

Line art by Creative Services Associates, Inc.

Contents

Series Overview

Introduction

The *Physical Science* series presents the diverse topics of matter, energy, machines, Newton's laws, chemical changes, magnets, light and sound, and force and motion. Each book builds core science concepts through carefully formatted texts designed to develop nonfiction reading skills.

The series uses a variety of genres, organizational patterns, and text and graphic features to help students learn how to successfully navigate nonfiction formats. At the same time, the series presents standards-based science content in a visually motivating format—infused with questions, process skill development, and hands-on activities that support science instruction in the classroom.

The organization of each book in the series helps students build a framework for comprehension:

The Introduction captures students' attention by giving them a real-life example of science in action.

Chapter 1 supplies students with the fundamental information needed for a broad understanding of the topic.

Chapter 2 provides an in-depth look at the topic.

Chapter 3 shows how scientists are exploring the topic today and what questions and challenges exist for future scientists.

The books in the *Physical Science* series also contain a variety of features that motivate students:

Picture This presents illustrations or photographs that help kids get the "big picture."

Thinking Like a Scientist introduces a process skill and then provides opportunities for practice.

Hands-On Science models a physical science experiment.

Science Notebook encourages further study with fun facts and additional resources to explore.

Focus on Literacy
Developing Comprehension Skills

Individual titles provide opportunities for students to develop, practice, and extend their repertoire of reading skills. Students have opportunities to adapt their skills to the different text structures, formats, and graphic elements that characterize nonfiction texts. The following skills are presented:

Identify main idea and details

Use context clues

Summarize

Draw conclusions

Compare and contrast

Use graphic organizers

Use specialized words

Paraphrase

Self-question

Identify cause-and-effect relationships

Understanding Nonfiction Genres, Text Features, and Graphics

Successful readers of informational text are adept at reading varied genres and formats. Being proficient at using the diverse characteristics of nonfiction texts is essential to understanding informational material. A variety of the nonfiction features are incorporated in the *Physical Science* series:

Genres

Expository	Procedural

Graphic Information

Photographs	Charts
Illustrations	Time Lines
Diagrams	

Parts of a Book

Contents	Index
Glossary	

Text Features

Chapter titles, subheads	Labels
Captions	Sidebars and features

Reading Across Texts

Recent research in student reading behaviors and proficiency indicates students' reading skills are enhanced when students have opportunities to read and compare multiple texts. This series provides an excellent opportunity to read varied texts on the same general theme—physical science. Students might want to discuss the following questions:

Compare—How are the books organized? How are book organizations alike and different?

Evaluate—Is the information presented clearly? What features are helpful in understanding a topic?

Generalize—What characteristics are shared by the topics of each book in the series? How are the topics different? How do they contribute to the overall understanding of physical-science concepts?

Focus on Science
Core Concepts

This series encourages students to read and wonder about energy, movement, and the physical world. Rather than covering a wide breadth of unrelated facts and topics, the series invites students to read deeply and explore related concepts. The titles in the *Physical Science* series provides students with the opportunity to read engaging nonfiction that teaches core concepts that support the National Science Education Standards, including the following:

PHYSICAL SCIENCE: Grades K–4
- Properties of objects and materials
- Position and motion of objects
- Light, heat, electricity, and magnetism

PHYSICAL SCIENCE: Grades 5–8
- Properties and changes of properties in matter
- Motions and forces
- Transfer of energy

HISTORY AND NATURE OF SCIENCE: Grades K–4, 5–8
- Science as a human endeavor

SCIENCE AS INQUIRY: Grades K–4, 5–8
- Abilities necessary to do scientific inquiry
- Understanding about scientific inquiry

SCIENCE IN PERSONAL AND SOCIAL PERSPECTIVES: Grades K–4, 5–8
- Populations, resources, and environments

SCIENCE AND TECHNOLOGY: Grades K–4, 5–8
- Understanding about science and technology

Developing Science Process Skills

Each *Physical Science* title provides students with opportunities to engage in scientific inquiry as they use scientific reasoning and critical thinking to develop their understanding of science. Each book in the *Physical Science* series features a science process skill that provides structured support for students as they develop their abilities to think in ways associated with scientific inquiry. Students are introduced to the process skill as they read and then practice the skill in the Thinking Like A Scientist feature. The following process skills are highlighted in the Physical Science series:

- Controlling Variables—*Machines Make It Move*
- Defining Operationally—*The Magic of Light and Sound*
- Experimenting—*Matter, Matter Everywhere*
- Inferring—*The Mystery of Magnets*
- Making a Model—*Understanding Electricity*
- Measuring—*Using Force and Motion, Introduction to Energy*
- Observing—*Chemical Changes*
- Predicting—*Acids and Bases, Newton's Laws*

Hands-On Science

A controlled experiment opens the door to in-depth learning in each title in the series:

- A Heat-Releasing Reaction (from *Chemical Changes*)
- Changing Matter (from *Matter, Matter Everywhere*)
- Energy Fun (from *Introduction to Energy*)
- How an Electrical System Works (from *Understanding Electricity*)
- Make Your Own Magnets (from *The Mystery of Magnets*)
- Newton's Laws in Action (from *Newton's Laws*)
- Turning an Inclined Plane into a Screw (from *Machines Make It Move*)
- The Sound of a Pin Dropping (from *The Magic of Light and Sound*)
- Force and Friction (from *Using Force and Motion*)
- What's the pH of Your Soap? (from *Acids and Bases*)

Overview The Overview page saves time in selecting books and planning instruction.

Summary
A brief summary highlights the main ideas and important details of the book.

Science Background
Additional information about the places, the people, and the science topics related to the book provides a context for the book.

Learning Objectives
Key learning objectives in nonfiction features and genre as well as reading, writing, and science process skills and strategies are listed to make planning efficient.

Overview

Acids and Bases

By Rebecca L. Johnson

Summary

We come across many acids and bases each day, from the food we eat to our household cleaners. Substances are classified as acids or bases, depending on their number of hydrogen ions. Each type of substance has specific characteristics that indicate whether it is an acid or a base. In nature, acids and bases are used by plants and animals to defend themselves.

The easiest way to tell an acid from a base is by using an indicator, such as litmus paper. The pH scale classifies substances with a pH less than 7 as acids and substances greater than 7 as bases. A universal indicator is needed to tell the pH of any substance. Many of the everyday items we use today are acids and bases, including soap, fabrics, and silicon chips.

Science Background

Almost all substances can be classified as acids or bases, depending on their pH. Acids have a pH in the range of 0 to 6.99, bases have a pH in the range of 7.01 to 14, and pure water is termed "neutral" with a pH of 7. The pH scale was developed by Soren Sorensen. The scale's name stands for "potential of hydrogen," which refers to the amount of hydrogen ions in a liquid. The more acidic a solution is, the fewer hydrogen ions it has.

Learning Objectives

Science

- Explain how substances are placed in categories according to their characteristics
- Identify properties of acids and bases
- Describe the harmful effects of acids and bases

- Describe methods of identifying acids and bases
- Identify common acids and bases

Process Skills

Skill Focus
- Predicting

Supporting Skills
- Communicating
- Inferring

Reading Skills

Genre: Expository

Skill Focus
- Compare and cont
- Use context clues

Supporting Skills
- Summarize
- Draw conclusions
- Identify cause-and effect relationship
- Make judgments

10 *Acids and Bases*

Focus on Reading Suggested activities help students develop strategies to use before, during, and after reading.

Focus on Reading

Before Reading

Activate Prior Knowledge

Direct students' attention to the title of the book. Ask them what they know about acids and bases. Begin a K-W-L chart for the class, writing information students know about acids and bases in the K (What We Know) column. Then ask students what they want to know about acids and bases. Write their responses in the W (What We Want to Know) column.

After reading, students can add information to the L (What We Learned) column. They can also change any incorrect information in the first column of the chart.

What We Know	What We Want To Know	What We Learned

Preview

Give students time to preview the book, paying attention to chapter titles, photos, captions, and special features. Ask:

What do the chapter titles tell you about the information presented in this book?

Looking at the photos, can you tell what this book is about?

What information do the captions provide?

Set Purpose

Ask students whether this book reminds them of other books they have read. Ask:

What do you want to find out by reading this book?

Encourage students to give reasons for their answers.

Vocabulary Strategy: Use Context Clues

Activity Master, Page 14

Ask students how context—the words around a word—can help them figure out the meaning of an unknown word. Read these sentences from page 5.

Acid drips from the snottites. It can burn skin and dissolve metal.

Explain that the descriptions "burn skin" and "dissolve metal" help provide a meaning for the word *acid* in the first sentence. The context of the word *acid* helps you to understand its meaning. Students can use the Activity Master on page 14 to practice taking meanings of words from context, then checking meanings in the glossary.

acid rain
fossil fuels
indicator
ions
pH
predict

Acids and Bases

Correlation to National Standards

Writing Skills	Science	Reading/Language Arts
Writing Focus • Write steps in a process (expository) **Supporting Skills** • Prewrite • Conduct research • Record knowledge **Speaking/Listening** • Give an oral presentation	• Properties of matter and changes of properties in matter (5–8) • Properties of objects and materials (K–4) • Personal health (K–4, 5–8) • Scientific inquiry (K–4, 5–8)	• Read to build an understanding of acids and bases • Read a wide range of literature • Apply a wide range of strategies to comprehend and interpret texts • Use spoken and written language for learning • Use the writing process

Acids and Bases 11

Activate Prior Knowledge
Graphic aids are often used to help organize prior knowledge.

Preview
Previewing nonfiction text helps students to understand how the text is organized and to anticipate what kinds of information will be included.

Vocabulary Strategy
Students use an Activity Master to work with content words prior to reading.

Correlation to National Standards
Content is correlated to national standards to ensure that key concepts are covered. A chart correlating all titles to national standards is on page 101 of this book.

Focus on Reading Suggested activities help students develop strategies to use before, during, and after reading.

Read Strategically
An Activity Master is provided to develop essential comprehension skills. The **Strategy Tip** offers concrete tips to help develop metacognitive strategies.

Meeting Individual Needs
Use the strategies starting on page 90 of this book to modify instruction to meet the needs of special populations.

Responding
Discussion questions help students to examine the main ideas included in each book.

Writing and Research
Students research topics and write in a variety of genres and forms.

Communicating
Activities help students develop the communication skills of listening, speaking, and viewing.

During Reading

 Read Strategically: Compare and Contrast
Activity Master, Page 15
Assign each chapter of the book as independent reading. As students read, they can compare and contrast characteristics of substances by completing the Activity Master on page 15.

Remind students that when comparing two things, they should look for what is the same. When contrasting two things, they should look for what is different

Answers for Activity Master, page 15: Acid—tastes sour, dissolves metal, turns blue litmus paper red, pH range: 0–7, contains hydrogen. Base—contains hydroxide, turns red litmus paper blue, feels slippery, tastes bitter, pH range: 7–14. Both—has industrial uses, is a chemical, some are poisonous, contains ions.

Strategy Tip: Paraphrase
If students have trouble understanding a paragraph or section of the book, suggest they retell, or paraphrase, the part in their own words. Explain that paraphrasing helps to identify which parts they don't understand.

 Meeting Individual Needs
For specific strategies on meeting individual needs, see pages 90–95.

After Reading

Responding
Initiate a class discussion to assess reading comprehension. Ask:

What characteristics are used to describe substances as acids or bases? (See pages 8 and 17 in the student book.) **(summarize)**

Describe the properties of acids. Describe the properties of bases. (See pages 9–11.) **(summarize)**

What are some harmful effects of acids and bases? (See pages 10 and 12–13.) **(draw conclusions)**

Which type of substance causes red litmus paper to turn blue? Which type of substance causes blue litmus paper to turn red? (See page 15.) **(identify cause-and-effect relationships)**

Which are more useful in your home—acids or bases? (Answers will vary.) **(make judgments)**

 Writing and Research: Write Steps in a Process
Activity Master, page 16
Have students write the steps involved in testing whether a substance is an acid or a base. Students will explain how they would test five liquids to determine if they are acids or bases. They will include step-by-step instructions, an explanation for each step, and the materials used in the process. Students can use the Activity Master on page 16 to help them organize the steps they would do in their

experiments. Encourage students to use science resources, the Internet, encyclopedias, and other informational sources to research the details of this process.

Communicating: Speaking/Listening

Give an oral presentation
Students can present an oral presentation showing the steps involved in testing a substance to determine if it is an acid or a base. Suggest that students use props, including posters or pictures, to help explain the steps in their process.

Students reading aloud should

✓ speak clearly
✓ make eye contact with listeners
✓ adapt speech as appropriate

Listeners should

✓ listen politely
✓ listen for clues to decide if the substance is an acid or a base
✓ ask questions to clarify information

Extend and Assess
A focus on science, assessment, and extension activities provides a variety of instructional options.

Extend and Assess

Focus on Science

Thinking Like a Scientist

Process Skill: Predicting

Answer for page 19: The pH of the juice would be 7, or closer to 7. To test this prediction, test the pH of a glass of orange juice before and after placing a crushed antacid tablet in the glass.

Answers for page 27: 1. The acid reduces the pH of your mouth. 2. The toothpaste will neutralize the acid in your mouth. 3. Since toothpaste is a base, it will raise the pH of your mouth.

Check It Out: Yes, it was a good idea. Baking soda is also a base, which will neutralize the acid in your mouth.

 Predicting
Activity Master, Page 17

Students list the characteristics of acids and bases on the Activity Master on page 17. Have them use the information and personal experience to predict the results for situations involving acids and bases.

Hands-on Science

Summary Students will use bar soap, water, and pH paper to check the pH of different soaps.

Tips Have students work over a desk or use a bowl to avoid messes involving the soap.

Safety Note Have students rinse their hands after handling soap. Remind them not to touch their eyes, mouth, or nose with soapy hands.

Answers to Think *Answers will vary, but the pH of the soap should be between 7 and 10; answers will vary depending on the brand of soap used; answers will vary, but no soap should have had a pH greater than 10, which would have been very basic and is rough on hands.*

Assessment Options

Use the following assessment options to assess students' understanding of the book.

Questions

Use the following questions during individual conferences or ask students to write the answers in their notebooks:

1 What is the pH range for acids? What is the pH range for bases?

2 Describe two physical properties of acids and two physical properties of bases.

3 Identify ways acids and bases can be harmful to humans.

4 Name a common acidic substances and a common basic substance.

Assessment Activity

Have students create an acids and bases poster. They can cut pictures of several common acids and bases from newspapers and magazines and glue them to poster board.

Posters should include

✓ three pictures of common acids and three pictures of common bases
✓ characteristics of the item that tell whether it is an acid or a base

Multiple-Choice Test

Use the multiple-choice test on page 106.

Cross-Curricular Connection

Mathematics

Have students create a pH scale as shown below. They can then insert each of the following on the scale where appropriate:

Stomach acid—pH 2
Apple—pH 3.5
Bread—pH 5.5
Baking soda—pH 9
Bleach—pH 13
Oven cleaner—pH 14

Ask students how the scale makes the pH data easier to compare than the list.

Home-School Connection

Together students and families can read the labels of common items in the home to determine whether each is an acid or a base. An acid often lists ingredients that include the word "acid." A base often has ingredients that include the word "hydroxide," or end in *-ide*.

Focus on Science
Activities developing key science concepts and skills help students understand the books in new ways. An Activity Master develops essential process skills.

Assessment
Use the discussion questions, the assessment activity, or the multiple-choice test to evaluate students' understanding of important concepts in the book.

Cross-Curricular Connection
Suggested activities provide opportunities to integrate science content with math, social studies, music, art, and literature.

Home-School Connection
Home-school connections offer ideas for students to talk about their work with family members.

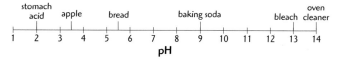

Acids and Bases 13

Acids and Bases

By Rebecca L. Johnson

Summary

We come across many acids and bases each day, from the food we eat to our household cleaners. Substances are classified as acids or bases, depending on their number of hydrogen ions. Each type of substance has specific characteristics that indicate whether it is an acid or a base. In nature, acids and bases are used by plants and animals to defend themselves.

The easiest way to tell an acid from a base is by using an indicator, such as litmus paper. The pH scale classifies substances with a pH less than 7 as acids and substances greater than 7 as bases. A universal indicator is needed to tell the pH of any substance. Many of the everyday items we use today are acids and bases, including soap, fabrics, and silicon chips.

Science Background

Almost all substances can be classified as acids or bases, depending on their pH. Acids have a pH in the range of 0 to 6.99, bases have a pH in the range of 7.01 to 14, and pure water is termed "neutral" with a pH of 7. The pH scale was developed by Soren Sorensen. The scale's name stands for "potential of hydrogen," which refers to the amount of hydrogen ions in a liquid. The more acidic a solution is, the fewer hydrogen ions it has.

Learning Objectives

Science

- Explain how substances are placed in categories according to their characteristics
- Identify properties of acids and bases
- Describe the harmful effects of acids and bases

- Describe methods of identifying acids and bases
- Identify common acids and bases

Process Skills

Skill Focus
- Predicting

Supporting Skills
- Communicating
- Inferring

Reading Skills

Genre: Expository

Skill Focus
- Compare and contrast
- Use context clues

Supporting Skills
- Summarize
- Draw conclusions
- Identify cause-and-effect relationships
- Make judgments

Focus on Reading

Before Reading

Activate Prior Knowledge

Direct students' attention to the title of the book. Ask them what they know about acids and bases. Begin a K-W-L chart for the class, writing information students know about acids and bases in the K (What We Know) column. Then ask students what they want to know about acids and bases. Write their responses in the W (What We Want to Know) column.

After reading, students can add information to the L (What We Learned) column. They can also change any incorrect information in the first column of the chart.

Preview

Give students time to preview the book, paying attention to chapter titles, photos, captions, and special features. Ask:

What do the chapter titles tell you about the information presented in this book?

Looking at the photos, can you tell what this book is about?

What information do the captions provide?

Set Purpose

Ask students whether this book reminds them of other books they have read. Ask:

What do you want to find out by reading this book?

Encourage students to give reasons for their answers.

Vocabulary Strategy: Use Context Clues

Activity Master, Page 14

Ask students how context—the words around a word—can help them figure out the meaning of an unknown word. Read these sentences from page 5.

Acid drips from the snottites. It can burn skin and dissolve metal.

Explain that the descriptions "burn skin" and "dissolve metal" help provide a meaning for the word *acid* in the first sentence. The context of the word *acid* helps you to understand its meaning. Students can use the Activity Master on page 14 to practice taking meanings of words from context, then checking meanings in the glossary.

acid rain
fossil fuels
indicator
ions
pH
predict

What We Know	What We Want To Know	What We Learned

Correlation to National Standards

Writing Skills

Writing Focus
- Write steps in a process (expository)

Supporting Skills
- Prewrite
- Conduct research
- Record knowledge

Speaking/Listening
- Give an oral presentation

Science

- Properties of matter and changes of properties in matter (5–8)
- Properties of objects and materials (K–4)
- Personal health (K–4, 5–8)
- Scientific inquiry (K–4, 5–8)

Reading/Language Arts

- Read to build an understanding of acids and bases
- Read a wide range of literature
- Apply a wide range of strategies to comprehend and interpret texts
- Use spoken and written language for learning
- Use the writing process

During Reading

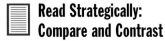 **Read Strategically: Compare and Contrast**

Activity Master, Page 15

Assign each chapter of the book as independent reading. As students read, they can compare and contrast characteristics of substances by completing the Activity Master on page 15.

Remind students that when comparing two things, they should look for what is the same. When contrasting two things, they should look for what is different.

Answers for Activity Master, page 15: Acid—tastes sour, dissolves metal, turns blue litmus paper red, pH range: 0–7, contains hydrogen. Base—contains hydroxide, turns red litmus paper blue, feels slippery, tastes bitter, pH range: 7–14. Both—has industrial uses, is a chemical, some are poisonous, contains ions.

Strategy Tip: Paraphrase

If students have trouble understanding a paragraph or section of the book, suggest they retell, or paraphrase, the part in their own words. Explain that paraphrasing helps to identify which parts they don't understand.

Meeting Individual Needs

For specific strategies on meeting individual needs, see pages 90–95.

After Reading

Responding

Initiate a class discussion to assess reading comprehension. Ask:

What characteristics are used to describe substances as acids or bases? (See pages 8 and 17 in the student book.) **(summarize)**

Describe the properties of acids. Describe the properties of bases. (See pages 9–11.) **(summarize)**

What are some harmful effects of acids and bases? (See pages 10 and 12–13.) **(draw conclusions)**

Which type of substance causes red litmus paper to turn blue? Which type of substance causes blue litmus paper to turn red? (See page 15.) **(identify cause-and-effect relationships)**

Which are more useful in your home—acids or bases? (Answers will vary.) **(make judgments)**

Writing and Research: Write Steps in a Process

Activity Master, page 16

Have students write the steps involved in testing whether a substance is an acid or a base. Students will explain how they would test five liquids to determine if they are acids or bases. They will include step-by-step instructions, an explanation for each step, and the materials used in the process. Students can use the Activity Master on page 16 to help them organize the steps they would do in their

experiments. Encourage students to use science resources, the Internet, encyclopedias, and other informational sources to research the details of this process.

Communicating: Speaking/Listening

Give an oral presentation

Students can present an oral presentation showing the steps involved in testing a substance to determine if it is an acid or a base. Suggest that students use props, including posters or pictures, to help explain the steps in their process.

Students reading aloud should

✓ speak clearly
✓ make eye contact with listeners
✓ adapt speech as appropriate

Listeners should

✓ listen politely
✓ listen for clues to decide if the substance is an acid or a base
✓ ask questions to clarify information

Extend and Assess

Focus on Science

Thinking Like a Scientist

Process Skill: Predicting

Answer for page 19: The pH of the juice would be 7, or closer to 7. To test this prediction, test the pH of a glass of orange juice before and after placing a crushed antacid tablet in the glass.

Answers for page 27: 1. The acid reduces the pH of your mouth. 2. The toothpaste will neutralize the acid in your mouth. 3. Since toothpaste is a base, it will raise the pH of your mouth.

Check It Out: Yes, it was a good idea. Baking soda is also a base, which will neutralize the acid in your mouth.

Predicting
Activity Master, Page 17

Students list the characteristics of acids and bases on the Activity Master on page 17. Have them use the information and personal experience to predict the results for situations involving acids and bases.

Hands-on Science

Summary Students will use bar soap, water, and pH paper to check the pH of different soaps.

Tips Have students work over a desk or use a bowl to avoid messes involving the soap.

Safety Note Have students rinse their hands after handling soap. Remind them not to touch their eyes, mouth, or nose with soapy hands.

Answers to Think Answers will vary, but the pH of the soap should be between 7 and 10; answers will vary depending on the brand of soap used; answers will vary, but no soap should have had a pH greater than 10, which would have been very basic and is rough on hands.

Assessment Options

Use the following assessment options to assess students' understanding of the book.

Questions

Use the following questions during individual conferences or ask students to write the answers in their notebooks:

1 What is the pH range for acids? What is the pH range for bases?

2 Describe two physical properties of acids and two physical properties of bases.

3 Identify ways acids and bases can be harmful to humans.

4 Name a common acidic substance and a common basic substance.

5 Describe two uses for acids and bases in society.

Assessment Activity

Have students create an acids and bases poster. They can cut pictures of several common acids and bases from newspapers and magazines and glue them to poster board.

Posters should include

✓ three pictures of common acids and three pictures of common bases

✓ characteristics of the item that tell whether it is an acid or a base

Multiple-Choice Test

Use the multiple-choice test on page 106.

Cross-Curricular Connection

Mathematics

Have students create a pH scale as shown below. They can then insert each of the following on the scale where appropriate:

Stomach acid—pH 2
Apple—pH 3.5
Bread—pH 5.5
Baking soda—pH 9
Bleach—pH 13
Oven cleaner—pH 14

Ask students how the scale makes the pH data easier to compare than the list.

Home-School Connection

Together students and families can read the labels of common items in the home to determine whether each is an acid or a base. An acid often lists ingredients that include the word "acid." A base often has ingredients that include the word "hydroxide," or end in *-ide*.

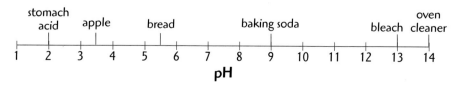

Vocabulary: Use Context Clues

The words below are from *Acids and Bases*. Find each word in the student book and read the sentence that contains the word and the sentences before and after. Write the meaning of each word based on how it is used in the book. Then use the glossary to check your answers.

Word	Meaning from Context	Definition from Glossary
acid rain		
fossil fuels		
indicator		
ions		
pH		
predict		

Vocabulary

Reading: Compare and Contrast

Acids and bases each have special characteristics that make them different. But they also have some characteristics in common. When you contrast two things, you tell how they are different. When you compare two things, you tell how they are the same.

As you read *Acids and Bases*, think about the characteristics of acids and bases. Each characteristic listed below describes acids, bases, or both. Write characteristics that apply only to acids in the left circle, only to bases in the right circle, and to both acids and bases in the overlapping portion of the circles.

Characteristics

- tastes sour
- has industrial uses
- dissolves metal
- contains hydroxide

- turns red litmus paper blue
- turns blue litmus paper red
- feels slippery

- is a chemical
- pH range: 0–7
- tastes bitter
- contains hydrogen

- some are poisonous
- contains ions
- pH range: 7–14

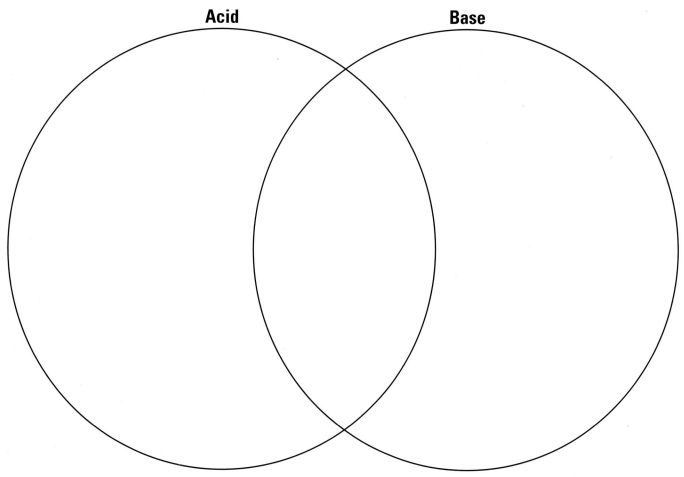

Acid   **Base**

Writing: Prewrite

Write Steps in a Process

When scientists do experiments, they write a list of materials they will need and the steps that they will do. Use the questions below to help you plan an experiment that will determine if five common liquids are acids or bases.

1. What liquids will you test in the experiment?

   _____

2. Would you use litmus paper or a universal indicator to tell if the liquids were acids or bases?

   _____

3. Using the testing method that you have chosen, how would you know if a liquid were an acid or a base?

   _____

   _____

4. What materials would you need to do your experiment?

   _____

   _____

5. List the steps that you would do to test each liquid to determine if it was an acid or a base.

   _____

   _____

6. Create a data table that you would use to show the results of your experiment.

Thinking Like a Scientist: Predicting

Substances have traits that can be used to tell whether the substance is an acid or a base. Use *Acids and Bases* and other sources to list characteristics of acids and bases. Then predict what would happen in each case.

Characteristics of Acids	**Characteristics of Bases**
• • •	• • •

1. Many household cleaners are bases. What would happen to the pH of water in a bucket if you added a cleaner?

   _____

   _____

2. Cola contains carbonic acid. What might happen if pennies were left in a glass of cola for a long time?

   _____

   _____

3. If your parent added milk to his or her coffee, would he or she make the coffee more acidic or more basic?

   _____

   _____

4. Milk of magnesia is a base. What would happen if you drank milk of magnesia for an upset stomach?

   _____

   _____

5. Choose one of the predictions above. How could you check the prediction you made?

   _____

   _____

Chemical Changes

By Rebecca L. Johnson

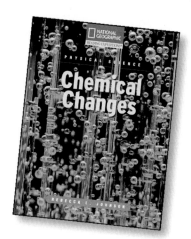

Summary

Matter can undergo physical and chemical changes. New substances are formed during chemical changes. During this process, energy is either absorbed and used to fuel a reaction or released as the result of a reaction. Because molecules are in constant motion, the rate at which a reaction takes place is largely determined by the rate at which molecules move and bump into one another. Raising the temperature of a substance is one way to speed reaction rate. Catalysts are chemical substances that speed chemical reactions. When chemical reactions occur, energy is given off or absorbed as the arrangement of atoms changes to form a new substance.

Science Background

During a chemical reaction, bonds that hold atoms together in a substance are broken and become rearranged. This rearranging of atoms and the creation of a new substance distinguishes chemical changes from physical changes. In a physical change, such as ice melting to water, the physical appearance may change, but no new substance is formed. Chemical reactions involve a change in energy. In some chemical reactions, energy is released to the environment. In others, energy is absorbed from the environment. Every chemical reaction requires some energy input to get started. This is the reaction's activation energy. Catalysts work by lowering the amount of activation energy needed for a reaction to proceed. This enables the reaction to take place more easily and speeds the overall reaction rate.

Learning Objectives

Science

- Distinguish between physical and chemical changes
- Understand that chemical reactions involve changes in energy
- Identify factors that affect reaction rate

- Explain the role of enzymes in chemical reactions
- Describe the importance of chemical reactions in daily life

Process Skills

Skill Focus
- Observing

Supporting Skills
- Communicating
- Inferring

Reading Skills

Genre: Expository

Skill Focus
- Draw conclusions
- Determine word knowledge

Supporting Skills
- Summarize
- Compare and contrast
- Reread

Focus on Reading

Before Reading

Activate Prior Knowledge

Ask students what they know about chemical changes and reactions. You might ask questions such as these:

What is a chemical change?

How is a chemical change different from a physical change?

Write students' ideas in a K-W-L chart on the board. Explain that in the first column, students will write what they know about chemical changes. In the second column, they will write what they want to know about chemical changes. In the third column, students will record what they learned after reading the book.

Preview

Give students time to flip through the book, paying attention to chapter titles, photos, captions, and diagrams. Ask:

What topics do you think will be included in this book?

What might you learn from the photographs and captions?

What might you learn from the diagram and text on pages 12 and 13?

Set Purpose

Ask students whether this book reminds them of other books they have read. Have them set a purpose for reading. Ask:

What do you want to find out from reading this book?

Vocabulary Strategy: Determine Word Knowledge
Activity Master, Page 22

Turn to page 5 and point out the word *element*. Ask students what they know about this word and write their replies on the board. Relate the word to chemical reactions by explaining that elements can join with other elements during chemical reactions to form new substances. Have students work with other words that relate to the topic of the book. On the Activity Master on page 22, students will write what they already know about each word. Then they will investigate the word and write a sentence relating each word to chemical reactions. Students will use these words:

atom
bond
catalyst
electron
molecule
product

What I Know	What I Want to Know	What I Learned

Correlation to National Standards

Writing Skills	Science	Reading/Language Arts
Writing Focus • Write steps in a process (expository) **Supporting Skills** • Prewrite • Conduct research • Record knowledge **Speaking/Listening** • Give an oral presentation	• Properties of objects and materials (K–4, 5–8) • Properties and changes of properties in matter (5–8) • Scientific inquiry (K–4, 5–8) • Nature of science (K–4, 5–8) • Science and technology (K–4, 5–8) • Science as a human endeavor (K–4, 5–8)	• Read to be informed • Apply a wide range of strategies to comprehend and interpret texts • Use a variety of informational resources • Apply language structure and conventions • Conduct research • Use the writing process

During Reading

 **Read Strategically:
Draw Conclusions**
Activity Master, Page 23

Assign each chapter of the book as independent reading. As they read, students can use the Activity Master on page 23 to draw conclusions about chemical reactions and their importance in daily life. Remind students that when they draw a conclusion, they make a decision about the facts they are given and what they already know.

Students should keep the following questions in mind:

How did I reach this conclusion?

Is the information accurate?

Does this conclusion make sense? Is it logical?

Are there other conclusions that make more sense?

Strategy Tip: Reread
Remind students to reread sections they are having difficulty understanding. If they are still having difficulty, students can ask for clarification during the follow-up discussion.

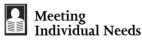 **Meeting
Individual Needs**
For specific strategies on meeting individual needs, see pages 90–95.

After Reading

Responding
Initiate a class discussion to assess reading comprehension. Ask:

What are reactants and products? (See page 7 in the student book.) **(summarize)**

How is a physical change different from a chemical change? (See page 8.) **(compare and contrast)**

What are some clues that energy is being released during a chemical reaction? (See page 11.) **(draw conclusions)**

How do cold temperatures keep food from spoiling? (See page 15.) **(draw conclusions)**

How does raising temperature affect reaction rate? (See page 16.) **(identify cause-and-effect relationships)**

How can the rate of a chemical reaction be changed? (See page 17.) **(summarize)**

What are catalysts? (See page 18.) **(summarize)**

What happens when photographic film is exposed to light? (See page 21.) **(cause and effect)**

What are some everyday examples of chemical reactions? (See page 22.) **(summarize)**

How can certain types of bacteria be used to clean up chemicals? (See page 24.) **(draw conclusions)**

Writing and Research: Steps in a Process
Activity Master, Page 24

Discuss with students the benefits of using hydrogen fuel cells as the power source for cars. Then remind students that the use of fuel cells for this purpose occurs in a series of steps. Have students describe how a hydrogen fuel cell works, using their book and other resources to assist with comprehension. Students can use the Activity Master on page 24 to help them organize their ideas.

Communicating: Speaking/Listening

Give an oral presentation
In small groups, students can read their descriptions of how a hydrogen fuel cell works.

Students reading should

✓ speak clearly
✓ make eye contact with listeners
✓ adapt speech as appropriate

Listeners should

✓ listen politely
✓ determine whether the description is accurate
✓ ask questions to clarify ideas they didn't understand

Extend and Assess

Focus on Science

Thinking Like a Scientist

Process Skill: Observing

Answer for page 19: Shaking mixes the two chemical substances and increases collisions between molecules, speeding the reaction.

Answers for page 27: 1. on a table by a window; sunlight 2. Sunlight shining on the paper caused a chemical reaction that has made the colors fade. 3. They were protected from the sunlight by the top page; the chemical reaction didn't occur in them.

Check It Out: Yes, by exposing the paper to sunlight in various ways.

Observing

Activity Master, Page 25

Students use the Activity Master to make observations of what is shown in a series of illustrations and then answer questions based on these observations.

Answers for Activity Master, page 25: 1. The paper is being torn. 2. The paper is broken into smaller pieces of paper. 3. The paper is being burned. 4. The paper is changed from paper to ash. 5. Figure B shows a chemical change because the paper is changed into a new substance—ash. 6. Figure A shows a physical change because the paper, although changed in size, is still paper.

Hands-on Science

Summary Students use a thermometer, water, and antacid tablets to observe an endothermic chemical reaction.

Tip Use cold water.

Safety Note Students should handle thermometers carefully to prevent breakage. Have paper towels available in case of spills.

Answers to Think *Starting and ending water temperatures may vary for individual groups. The temperature of the water fell by the end of the experiment. An endothermic reaction took place because the temperature was lower at the end of the experiment; the reaction absorbed energy.*

Assessment Options

Use the following assessment options to assess students' understanding of *Chemical Changes.*

Questions

Use the following questions during individual conferencing or ask students to write the answers in their notebooks:

1 What is a chemical reaction?

2 What are the substances formed by a chemical reaction called?

3 What are some signs that a chemical reaction is occurring or has occurred?

4 What role does energy have in chemical reactions?

5 How does temperature affect chemical reactions?

Assessment Activity

Have students use the text or other resources to research a common chemical reaction. Students should create a poster that illustrates and explains the reaction they selected. They can either draw pictures or use pictures from a magazine on their posters. Their posters should have captions that include at least three words from the glossary.

Posters should

✓ use captions that include at least three words from the glossary
✓ use captions to explain the chemical reaction depicted
✓ use correct grammar and mechanics
✓ be well-organized and carefully prepared

Multiple-Choice Test

Use the multiple-choice test on page 107.

Cross-Curricular Connection

Mathematics

Explain to students that during a chemical reaction, matter is not created or destroyed. Thus, the mass of the reactants at the beginning of the reaction must be equal to the mass of the products resulting from the reaction. Have students use this information to identify how much sugar is produced in a chemical reaction involving 20 grams of carbon and 30 grams of water.

Home-School Connection

Students can discuss with family members the main ideas from *Chemical Changes.* Then students and family members can use this information to identify common chemical reactions and physical changes in matter that they observe in their daily lives.

Vocabulary: Determine Word Knowledge

Each word listed below is related to a chemical reaction. In the second column, write what you already know about each word. Use *Chemical Changes* and the glossary to find new information about each word. Then write a sentence relating each word to chemical reactions.

Word	What I Already Know	My Sentence About Chemical Reactions
atom		
bond		
catalyst		
electron		
molecule		
product		

Reading: Draw Conclusions

When you draw a conclusion, you make a decision that is based on the information you have been given and on what you already know. Write answers to the questions listed to draw conclusions.

1. Are chemical reactions important in keeping you alive and healthy? How?

_____

_____

2. What happens to matter involved in a chemical reaction?

_____

_____

3. When wood burns in a fireplace, what are some clues that tell you a chemical reaction is occurring?

_____

_____

4. How will lowering the temperature of a substance affect reaction rate?

_____

_____

5. What are some ways chemical reactions improve your daily life?

_____

_____

Check Your Thinking

- How did I reach this conclusion?

- Is the information I used accurate?

- Does this conclusion make sense? Is it logical?

- Are there other conclusions that make more sense?

Writing: Prewriting

Steps in a Process

Several steps are involved in generating energy from hydrogen through the use of a hydrogen fuel cell. Make sure that you understand the steps in this process. Then write four steps to explain how a hydrogen fuel cell works. You can use *Chemical Changes* and other resources to make sure that you understand the process. When writing each step, focus on how hydrogen is changed. Use the space below to list the details involved in each step.

Step 1:

_____

_____

_____

_____

Step 2:

_____

_____

_____

_____

Step 3:

_____

_____

_____

_____

Step 4:

_____

_____

_____

_____

Name _____

Thinking Like a Scientist: Observing

Observing, or using your senses to gather information, is an important skill in science. Carefully observe the two figures below. Then use your observations and your knowledge of chemical reactions to answer the questions.

Figure A

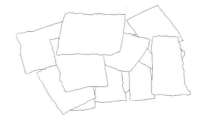

Start: Whole piece of paper   Finish: Many pieces of paper

Figure B

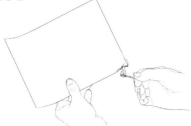

Start: Whole piece of paper   Finish: Ash

1. Look at Figure A. Describe what is happening in the first panel (the panel labeled Start).

    _____

2. In Figure A, how does the action change the paper?

    _____

3. Describe what is happening in the first panel of Figure B.

    _____

4. How does the action in Figure B change the paper?

    _____

5. Which figure shows a chemical change? How do you know?

    _____

6. Which figure shows a physical change? How do you know?

    _____

Science Skills   *Activity Master* 25

Introduction to Energy

By Glen Phelan

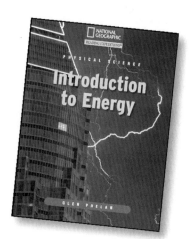

Summary

People use energy every day. Energy is the ability to do work, or move an object with a force. Most of the energy used on Earth ultimately comes from the sun. For example, the energy we use to move comes from the food we eat, which depends on the heat and light energy of the sun. Whenever energy changes form, such as from chemical to electrical energy, heat is given off. Experiments in the 18th and 19th centuries showed that heat, too, is energy. Heat energy moves from a warmer object to a cooler object. Different types of insulation help control temperatures in buildings, animals, and people by reducing the transfer of heat.

Science Background

There are two general kinds of energy: kinetic (energy of motion) and potential (stored energy). Kinetic and potential energy have a variety of forms. Some of these forms are electrical, chemical, and heat energy. Energy frequently changes, or converts, from one form to another. For example, a blown-up balloon has potential energy. If you let go of the balloon, the potential energy converts to kinetic energy as air escapes and sends the balloon flying. A battery works because of energy conversion. A typical battery, or dry cell, contains a moist paste that stores chemical energy. When the positive and negative terminals of the dry cell are connected in a circuit, the chemical energy converts to electrical energy. Any form of energy can be converted into any other form.

Learning Objectives

Science

- Describe the relationship between energy and work
- Explain the difference between energy of motion and stored energy
- Identify situations in which energy is transferred
- Describe different forms of energy
- Explain how heat is related to motion

Process Skills

Skill Focus
- Measuring

Supporting Skills
- Observing
- Communicating
- Collecting and interpreting data

Reading Skills

Genre: Expository

Skill Focus
- Identify cause-and-effect relationships
- Use specialized words

Supporting Skills
- Summarize
- Make judgments
- Compare and contrast
- Draw conclusions

Focus on Reading

Before Reading

Activate Prior Knowledge

Walk across the room and turn the light switch on and off. Pick up a pencil and drop it on the floor. Hold up a pinwheel or sheet of paper and blow on it so that students can watch it move. Let students know that everything you did involved energy. Ask students to name other actions that involve energy. You might ask questions such as these:

How have you used energy today?

Do you use energy even when you're sitting still?

What forces of nature involve energy?

As students discuss the answers to these questions, list their responses on the board. After reading, students can go back to their lists and add other ideas about energy.

Preview

Lead students as they preview the book. Draw their attention to chapter titles, headings, photos, captions, and sidebars. Ask:

What do the chapter titles tell you about the information in the book? What do you know about energy from the chapter titles?

What do the photos tell you about energy? Where can you find energy in nature? Where can you find energy in your own home?

Set Purpose

Ask students whether this book reminds them of other books they have read. Help students set a purpose for reading. Ask:

What do you want to find out about energy as you read?

Encourage students to give reasons for their answers. Model your own purpose for reading, such as *I want to read to learn about different kinds of energy.*

Vocabulary Strategy: Use Specialized Words

Activity Master, Page 30

Point out to students that the vocabulary words are in bold type. Explain that all of these words are used to describe energy and motion. Words that are used to describe a specific topic are called specialized words. Have students use the Activity Master on page 30 to explore some of the specialized words in this book. They can use the book and the glossary to explain how each of these words relates to energy and motion. Students will use the following words:

chemical energy
electrical energy
energy of motion
insulation
stored energy
transfer
work

Correlation to National Standards

Writing Skills	Science	Reading/Language Arts
Writing Focus • Write a letter (persuasive) **Supporting Skills** • Use the writing process • Write for different purposes • Respond to others' writing **Speaking/Listening** • Give an oral presentation	• Abilities of technological design (K–4, 5–8) • Understanding about science and technology (K–4, 5–8) • Light, heat, electricity and magnetism (K–4) • Motions and forces (5–8) • Transfer of energy (5–8)	• Read to build an understanding of different types of energy and the storing and transfer of energy • Apply a wide range of strategies to comprehend and interpret texts • Adjust use of written language to communicate effectively • Conduct research on issues by generating ideas and questions

During Reading

 Read Strategically: Identify Cause-and-Effect Relationships

Activity Master, Page 31

Assign each chapter of the book as independent reading. Have students use the Activity Master on page 31 to record information about causes and effects relating to motion and energy. Tell students that an effect is something that happens and a cause is the reason that something happens. Identifying causes and effects helps students see the connections between events.

Strategy Tip: Self-Question

Remind students that asking questions is a good way to set a purpose for reading. Students can preview a chapter by looking at the title, captions, photos, and headings. They can use the information they find to write questions that will guide their reading. Using the heading and photos on pages 8 and 9, for example, students might ask *What is stored energy? How does the airplane use stored energy?* Students can write their questions in their notebooks and record their answers as they read. Explain that not all questions may be answered and that students might think of new questions as they read.

 Meeting Individual Needs

For specific strategies on meeting individual needs, see pages 90–95.

After Reading

Responding

Initiate a class discussion to assess reading comprehension. Ask:

What is work? How is work related to energy? (See page 7 in the student book.) **(summarize)**

How does a soccer ball get its energy of motion? (See page 10.) **(identify cause-and-effect relationships)**

Describe three different forms of energy. Tell how they are alike and how they are different. (See pages 11–15.) **(compare and contrast)**

What might you conclude about a bike with warm tires? How did the tires become warm? (See pages 18–19.) **(draw conclusions)**

Why is it useful to learn about insulation? (See pages 22–25.) **(make judgments)**

 Writing and Research: Write a Persuasive Letter

Activity Master, Page 32

Point out that some of the sources of energy mentioned in this book, such as electrical and chemical energy, come from coal, oil, natural gas, and other nonrenewable sources. Some nonrenewable energy sources cause pollution, such as acid rain, and possibly contribute to global warming. Invite students to research renewable and nonrenewable energy sources. Have them write persuasive letters to convince someone to use renewable energy, nonrenewable energy, or both. They could write a letter to the editor of a newspaper or a letter to a city planner in their community. The Activity Master on page 32 will guide students in organizing their thoughts.

Communicating: Speaking/Listening

Give an oral presentation

In small groups, students can read their articles.

Students reading should

✓ speak clearly
✓ make eye contact with listeners
✓ adapt speech as appropriate

Listeners should

✓ listen politely
✓ ask questions to clarify ideas they didn't understand

Extend and Assess

Focus on Science

Thinking Like a Scientist

Process Skill: Measuring
Answers for page 21: 35°F, 2°C

Answers for page 27: 1. Monday: 72°F, 22°C; Tuesday: 84°F, 28°C 2. Yes, those numbers are included on these thermometer scales. 3. No, those numbers are not shown on these thermometer scales.

Check It Out: Showing every degree Fahrenheit would require so many lines on the scale that it would be difficult to read the scale.

Measuring
Activity Master, Page 33

Students use charts on the Activity Master on page 33 to examine data about heat index. They explore the relationship between temperature and humidity and its effects on the human body.

Hands-on Science

Summary Students use static electricity—a type of electrical energy—to make a balloon move an aluminum can. Then they use heat energy to partially inflate a balloon.

Tips For the rolling can activity, students can rub the balloon on their hair or clothing. For the pop-up balloon activity, the balloon may not inflate enough to stand up if the water is not warm enough. Adding a little hot tap water to the bowl should make the balloon stand up.

Safety Note Caution students to be careful when using hot water.

Answer to Think *In the rolling can activity, electrical energy changes to energy of motion. In the pop-up balloon activity, heat energy changes to energy of motion.*

Assessment Options

Use the following assessment options to assess students' understanding of *Introduction to Energy.*

Questions

Use the following questions during individual conferences, or ask students to write the answers in their notebooks:

1 Give an example of stored energy changing into energy of motion.

2 Describe how energy is transferred when a bat hits a baseball.

3 Explain the relationship between motion and heat.

4 What is happening to the water particles when a puddle on the ground evaporates?

5 How does a space suit keep astronauts from getting too warm or too cold?

Assessment Activity

Students can summarize what they found out about energy by creating a web. In the middle of the web, they can write "energy." They can surround the topic of energy by writing the different types of energy and a fact about each. Students can use words, pictures, or drawings to demonstrate their understanding of energy.

Webs should

✓ clearly convey ideas about energy
✓ be carefully and neatly prepared, clearly showing relationships between ideas
✓ present accurate facts

Multiple-Choice Test

Use the multiple-choice test on page 108.

Cross-Curricular Connection

Social Studies

Different places in the world experience extreme temperatures. In Libya, for example, the highest temperature recorded was 135.9°F (57.7°C). Antarctica's lowest temperature was −128.6°F (−89.2°C). Challenge students to find out more about temperatures in various places around the world and the ways in which people adapt to these climates. Students can report their findings on illustrated maps.

Home-School Connection

Have students work with their families to list objects or actions that use different types of energy in the course of a day. They may list electrical appliances, food, playing games, or walking up the stairs. As an alternative, students can work with their families to list ways that they can conserve energy in their homes.

Vocabulary: Use Specialized Words

The words below are from *Introduction to Energy*. Each word or term has something to do with energy. In each box, write a meaning for the word. Then use each word to write a sentence about energy. Use *Introduction to Energy* and the glossary to help you.

Word	Meaning	My Sentence
chemical energy		
electrical energy		
energy of motion		
insulation		
stored energy		
transfer		
work		

Reading: Identify Cause-and-Effect Relationships

As you read *Introduction to Energy*, think about how things change and what causes those changes. Think about how energy changes from one form to another and how energy causes things to happen. Then complete the chart below. Use the word "energy" in each box.

What happens? (Effect)	**Why does it happen? (Cause)**
1. A soccer ball flies down the field.	
2. You hear thunder.	
3. Ice cream melts.	
4. A flashlight shines.	
5. A well-insulated house stays warm in winter.	
6. A sailboat moves.	

Writing: Use the Writing Process

Write a Letter

Coal, oil, and natural gas store chemical energy that people use to provide heat and electricity. These energy sources are cheap but nonrenewable. When they are used up, they are not easily replaced. They also cause pollution. Renewable sources of energy, such as the sun and wind, are easily replaced. Most forms of renewable energy do not cause pollution. But they are often expensive. Research to find out more about renewable and nonrenewable resources.

Write a letter in which you try to persuade someone to use renewable energy sources, nonrenewable sources, or some of each. Use the space below to plan your letter.

1. What are some of the advantages and disadvantages of using nonrenewable energy sources?

Advantages	Disadvantages

2. What are some of the advantages and disadvantages of using renewable energy sources?

Advantages	Disadvantages

3. Use another sheet of paper to write your letter. Do these things.

   ✓ State your opinion in the beginning of your letter.

   ✓ List reasons to support your opinion.

   ✓ Include facts and examples to support your opinion.

   ✓ Be polite.

Thinking Like a Scientist: Measuring

Extreme heat is dangerous. In fact, in an average year, about 175 people in the United States die from the heat. To help people figure out when it is too hot to be outside for long periods of time, the National Weather Service created the Heat Index Chart. The Heat Index tells how hot it feels outside based on measurements: the temperature of the air and the relative humidity, or moisture in the air. Use the chart below to answer the questions.

Relative Humidity (%)

Heat Index (Apparent Temperature)

With Prolonged Exposure and/or Physical Activity

Air Temp (°F)	40	45	50	55	60	65	70	75	80	85	90	95	100
110	136												
108	130	137											
106	124	130	137										
104	119	124	131	137									
102	114	119	124	130	137								
100	109	114	113	124	129	136							
98	105	109	119	117	123	128	134						
96	101	104	108	112	116	121	126	132					
94	97	100	101	106	110	114	119	124	129	136			
92	94	96	99	101	105	108	112	116	121	126	131		
90	91	93	95	97	100	103	106	109	113	117	122	127	132
88	88	89	91	93	95	98	100	100	106	110	113	117	121
86	85	87	88	89	91	93	95	97	100	102	105	108	112
84	83	84	85	86	88	89	90	92	94	96	98	100	103
82	81	82	83	84	84	85	86	88	89	90	91	93	95
80	80	80	81	81	82	82	83	84	84	85	86	86	87

Extreme Danger: Heatstroke or sunstroke highly likely

Danger: Sunstroke, muscle cramps, and/or heat exhaustion likely

Extreme Caution: Sunstroke, muscle cramps, and/or heat exhaustion possible

Caution: Fatigue possible

1. When the temperature is 92°F, what is the heat index if the relative humidity is 65%?

_____

2. The relative humidity is 55%, and the heat index is 97. What is the air temperature?

_____

3. The heat index is 119, and the air temperature is 94°F. What is the relative humidity?

_____

4. If the air temperature is 80°F, can humidity make conditions extremely dangerous? Explain why or why not.

_____

_____

Machines Make it Move

By Rebecca L. Johnson

Summary

Machines make things move and help people get work done. Throughout history, people have used machines of different types to accomplish their goals, from building the great pyramids to pumping water out of the ground. The six types of simple machines are the wedge, the lever, the inclined plane, the screw, the wheel and axle, and the pulley. Each of these machines does at least one of the following: increases speed, increases available force, or changes the direction of force. These simple machines are used to make compound machines. Compound machines are used in all aspects of modern society. People today depend on machines in every part of their lives: at school, in the home, at work, and at play.

Science Background

Throughout history, people have faced the challenges of moving large objects and doing difficult work. In an attempt to make labor-intensive work easier, humans have invented machines to help them. Some machines are very complex with many moving parts. Others are far simpler. Even though simple machines don't look sophisticated, they have been used for centuries to perform a variety of tasks—from building the pyramids in Egypt to turning on a modern-day faucet.

Learning Objectives

Science

- Identify the six simple machines
- Explain how people build machines to solve certain problems
- Explain how ancient engineers used simple machines in their work
- Explain how the position and motion of objects can be changed by pushing or pulling
- Relate the size of change in position and motion to the strength of the push or pull

Process Skills

Skill Focus
- Controlling variables

Supporting Skills
- Observing
- Communicating
- Inferring
- Predicting

Reading Skills

Genre: Expository

Skill Focus
- Draw conclusions
- Use context clues

Supporting Skills
- Identify main idea and details
- Compare and contrast
- Use images to aid comprehension

Focus on Reading

Before Reading

Activate Prior Knowledge

Point out the title of the book and explain that the title helps define what machines are and what they do. Have students flip through the book to review the photographs. Ask:

What are some machines that make something move?

As appropriate, write students' responses in a web on the board labeled *Machines that make something move.* Explain to students that machines also help people get work done. Ask:

What are some machines that help get work done at home or in school?

As appropriate, write students' responses into a web on the board labeled *Machines that get work done at home or in school.* Have students copy the webs into their notebooks. Explain that the book they are about to read describes different types of machines and how they work.

Preview

Give students time to flip through the book, paying attention to chapter titles, photos, captions, and diagrams. Ask:

After looking at photos and reading captions, what topics do you think will be included in this book?

What kinds of information do the sidebars provide?

Look at the diagrams on pages 10, 14, 15, and 21. What do these diagrams show? What do the arrows help show?

Set Purpose

Ask students whether this book reminds them of other books they have read. Help them set a purpose for reading. Ask:

What do you want to find out by reading this book?

Vocabulary Strategy: Use Context Clues

Activity Master, Page 38

Have students turn to page 11. Point out the word *variables* and have a volunteer read the sentence with that word and the sentence that follows. Ask:

After reading this sentence and the sentence that follows, what do you think the word variable means?

Ask students to explain how they figured out the definition. Explain that using context clues, or the words around the word you don't know, is a good strategy for figuring out what an unfamiliar word means. Students can practice the strategy using these words:

- axle
- compound machine
- fulcrum
- gear
- lever
- pulley
- ramp

Correlation to National Standards

Writing Skills	Science	Reading/Language Arts
Writing Focus • Write directions (expository) • Prewrite **Supporting Skills** • Write for a specific audience • Conduct research **Speaking and Listening** • Give an oral presentation	• Position and motion of objects (K–4) • Scientific inquiry (K–4, 5–8) • Science and technology (K–4, 5–8) • Science as a human endeavor (K–4, 5–8) • Motions and forces (5–8) • Transfer of energy (5–8)	• Read to be informed and to build an understanding of modern society • Apply a wide range of strategies to comprehend and interpret texts • Apply language structure and conventions • Use the writing process • Conduct research • Participate in literacy communities • Use a variety of informational resources

During Reading

 ### Read Strategically: Draw Conclusions

Activity Master, Page 39

Assign each chapter of the book as independent reading. As they read, students can use the Activity Master on page 39 to draw conclusions about how machines are used. Remind students that when they draw a conclusion, they make a decision about something based on the facts they're given and what they already know. Explain that they draw conclusions on their own every day. In this case, they'll draw conclusions based on the facts in the book.

Strategy Tip: Use images to aid comprehension

Every image in *Machines Make It Move* supports the text in some way. Suggest that students "read" the photos and diagrams to help them more fully comprehend the book. They can ask questions as they do this:

What part of the text does this photo (or diagram) help explain?

Does this diagram match my understanding of how this machine works?

How do labels and captions help me understand?

 ### Meeting Individual Needs

For specific strategies on meeting individual needs, see pages 90–95.

After Reading

Responding

Initiate a class discussion to assess reading comprehension. Ask:

Why do people create and use machines? (See page 7 in the student book.) **(identify main idea and details)**

What is the difference between a simple machine and a compound machine? Give an example of each. (See pages 5–7.) **(compare and contrast)**

What are the six simple machines? (See pages 8–17.) **(retell)**

What are some examples of simple machines that were used in ancient times? How were they each used, and by whom? (See pages 5, 8–11, 13–14, and 17.) **(identify cause-and-effect relationships)**

Explain three ways you use simple machines in your daily life. (Answers will vary.) **(identify main idea and details)**

Why might the human body be called a "compound machine"? (See page 22.) **(summarize)**

Why do scientists control variables during experiments? (See pages 11 and 26–27.) **(draw conclusions)**

 ### Writing and Research: Write a User's Manual

Activity Master, Page 40

Many machines have user's manuals so that people can understand how the machines work and how they should be used. Students can create a simple user's manual for a machine of their choosing. They should include a simple illustration of the machine, labeling the parts of the machine. Students should then write brief instructions explaining how the machine should be used.

Suggest that students use *Machines Make It Move* and other resources to gather information for their manuals. Students can use the Activity Master on page 40 to help them choose a topic and generate ideas for their manuals.

Communicating: Speaking/Listening

Give an oral presentation

Students can present their manuals in small groups. After listeners provide feedback, allow students time to revise their manuals as needed.

Students reading should

- speak clearly
- make eye contact with listeners
- adapt speech patterns, such as insert pauses in appropriate places

Listeners should

- follow the progress of each step
- ask questions to clarify ideas
- make suggestions for making the directions easier to understand
- listen politely

Focus on Science

Thinking Like a Scientist

Process Skill: Controlling Variables
Answers for page 27: Students might suggest that the shape of the screw allows for a gradual change in elevation over many turns. Roads on hills often have many turns in them for the same reason.

 Controlling Variables

Activity Master, Page 41

Students use the Activity Master to evaluate the variables in a student's experiment. To do so, they must consider which variables should be controlled, which should be changed, and how these decisions will affect the outcome of the experiment.

Hands-on Science

Summary Students create models of three screws from inclined planes with different slopes. The paper-and-pencil model helps illustrate how screws are inclined planes that are twisted around a bar.

Tips Remind students to include the black line on each inclined plane to help them identify the threads of the screw when each inclined plane is wrapped around the pencil. Also, remind students to write their measurements directly on the inclined planes.

Answers to Think *The steepest inclined plane results in a screw with threads farthest apart. The 6-cm inclined plane would be the easiest to screw because its threads are the closest together.*

Assessment Options

Use the following assessment options to assess students' understanding.

Questions

Use the following questions during individual conferences or ask students to write the answers in their notebooks:

1 What are two reasons people use machines?

2 Explain how ancient people used simple machines.

3 Choose four simple machines and explain how they can be used.

4 Name two compound machines and explain how simple machines make them work.

5 Why do scientists want to control variables in experiments?

Assessment Activity

Ask students to create a poster about three simple machines. They should illustrate the basic principle behind each machine and provide an example of how this machine is used.

Posters should
✓ clearly present three simple machines and how they work
✓ include examples of each simple machine
✓ be well-organized and carefully prepared
✓ include a title
✓ use correct grammar and mechanics

Multiple-Choice Test

See the multiple-choice test on page 109.

Cross-Curricular Connection

Social Studies

Ask students to think about how machines have changed people's lives at home, at work, in transportation, and for communication. Students can make a chart with four headings and list appropriate machines in each column.

Home-School Connection

Have students list and describe to family members the six simple machines. Then students and family members can challenge one another to find the most examples of each simple machine in and around their homes.

Vocabulary: Use Context Clues

The words below are from *Machines Make It Move*. Find each word in the student book and read the sentence that contains the word and the sentences before and after. Write the meaning of each word based on how it is used in the book. Then use the glossary to check your answers.

Word	Meaning from Context	Definition from Glossary
axle		
compound machine		
fulcrum		
gear		
lever		
pulley		
ramp		

Reading: Draw Conclusions

When you draw a conclusion, you make a decision about something based on the information you are given and on what you already know. Write answers to these questions to draw conclusions.

How were simple machines used by people in ancient times?

_____

_____

Why are simple machines important to people today?

_____

_____

Why do compound machines "really get our world moving"?

_____

_____

Does each of the six simple machines have more than one use? Explain.

_____

_____

Why is the human body sometimes called the "human machine"?

_____

_____

Check Your Thinking

1. How did I reach this conclusion?

2. Is the information I used accurate?

3. Does this conclusion make sense? Is it logical?

4. Are there other conclusions that make more sense?

Writing: Prewriting

Write a User's Manual

Imagine that you are going to write a manual to explain how a person should use a machine. Choose a machine from the list below or a machine of your own. Keep in mind that you would be writing directions that should be easy for someone to follow.

You might need to gather information about how your machine works. Use *Machines Make It Move*, the Internet, and any other resources to find out more about your topic. Use the space below to organize your ideas for writing. Use other paper if you need more steps for your directions.

List of Topics: Choose One		**Other ideas:**
weighing scales	blender	_____
boat trailer	seesaw	_____
wheelbarrow	hand-held can opener	_____

My topic will be _____

Part 1: Simple illustration of my topic, including labels of

important parts _____

simple machines _____

Part 2: This is what my machine is used for:

_____

_____

Part 3: These are the steps that tell how this machine should be used:

Step 1: _____

Step 2: _____

Step 3: _____

Step 4: _____

Step 5: _____

Thinking Like a Scientist: Controlling Variables

Scientists do experiments to find answers to their questions. They must control the variables, or the different parts of the experiment, to find answers. Read the information about Claire's experiment. Then answer the questions.

Claire is experimenting with levers. She will use two friends and a seesaw in her experiment. Claire wants to know if the location of where her friends sit on the seesaw will affect how easy it is for one person to lift the other.

For the first part of Claire's experiment, she asks two friends to sit an equal distance from the fulcrum. She notices that the two friends are balanced and move up and down easily.

Now Claire wants to begin the second part of her experiment.
This is her question: Will the location of where one person sits affect how easy it is for him or her to lift the other person?

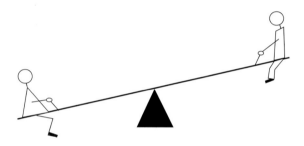

Questions

1. Should Claire use two friends who are the same weight? Why or why not?

2. What variable should Claire change for the second part of her experiment?

3. What parts of the experiment should stay the same for the second part?

4. What do you think Claire will learn from this experiment? Why?

5. How can Claire check her results?

Overview

Matter, Matter Everywhere

By Stephen M. Tomecek

Summary

Matter is anything that has mass and takes up space. Matter can exist in four states: solid, gas, liquid, and plasma. The properties of matter include mass, volume, and density. Each of these properties can be measured, which helps people describe and classify matter. Over time, scientists have learned about matter by conducting experiments. Scientists have learned that atoms are the building blocks of matter and that an element is a substance that is made of only one type of atom. Scientists have organized the elements in the Periodic Table of Elements based on the elements' atomic properties. Classifying matter in this way helps people understand the properties of elements and similarities in their structures.

Science Background

In this century many advancements have been made regarding our understanding of matter. Scientists have developed particle accelerators to learn more about atoms—the basic structures that make up all matter. Each year we are learning more about atoms and finding new ways to use physical and chemical changes to do work. As we learn more about matter, it is important to remember that our knowledge of matter has its roots in the past. Many men and women throughout history have influenced and expanded our understanding of the properties and structure of matter.

Learning Objectives

Science

- Explain how properties are used to classify and describe matter
- Identify tools used to measure properties
- Explain how matter can exist in different states: solid, liquid, gas, and plasma
- Compare chemical changes to physical changes in matter

- Describe how the periodic table organizes elements
- Recognize that atoms make up all living and nonliving things
- Differentiate atoms and compounds
- Identify scientists who have contributed to the field of chemistry

Process Skills

Skill Focus
- Experimenting

Supporting Skills
- Observing
- Communicating
- Interpreting
- Predicting

Reading Skills

Genre: Expository

Skill Focus
- Identify main idea and details
- Relate words

Supporting Skills
- Compare and contrast
- Summarize
- Self-question

Focus on Reading

Before Reading

Activate Prior Knowledge

Direct students' attention to the title of the book, explaining that matter is indeed everywhere around them. Matter is everything that has mass and takes up space. Many of the objects that students can see are solids, but matter can exist in the form of liquids, gases, and plasma, too. Discuss states of matter, using water as an example. Ask:

In what states of matter can water be found around your house?

If necessary, ask probing questions such as:

For example, in what form is water when you drink it?
(liquid)

Create a web based on students' responses.

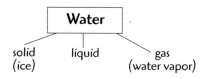

Review the concept that matter is everywhere and can be in different forms. Then discuss that the book they are about to read will give them a closer look at matter and explain how matter can be changed and used.

Preview

Give students time to flip through the book, paying attention to chapter titles, photos, captions, and diagrams. Ask:

After looking at photos and reading captions, what topics do you think will be included in this book?

What information does the chart on page 12 provide? What should you do if you don't understand words included in a chart?

What can you learn from the time line on pages 20–21?

Set Purpose

Ask students whether this book reminds them of other books they have read. Help students set a purpose for reading. Ask:

What do you want to find out by reading this book?

Vocabulary Strategy: Relate Words

Activity Master, Page 46

Have students turn to page 7 in the student book. Read the first paragraph to the class. Point out the word *matter* and ask:

Can you list other examples of matter based on the definition?

Explain to students that the vocabulary words in the book all relate to matter in some way. Have students use *Matter, Matter Everywhere*, the glossary, and a dictionary to write how each word relates to matter. Students will be using these words:

atom
chemistry
gas
liquid
mass
state
volume

Correlation to National Standards

Writing Skills	Science	Reading/Language Arts
Writing Focus • Write a report (expository) • Prewrite **Supporting Skills** • Use an outline • Conduct research **Viewing** • Analyze an image	• Scientific inquiry (K–4, 5–8) • Properties of objects and materials (K–4) • Properties and changes of properties in matter (5–8) • Science and technology (K–4, 5–8) • Science as a human endeavor (K–4, 5–8) • Nature of science (K–4, 5–8)	• Read to be informed • Apply a wide range of strategies to comprehend and interpret texts • Apply language structure and conventions • Use the writing process • Conduct research • Use a variety of informational resources

During Reading

 Read Strategically: Identify Main Idea and Details

Activity Master, Page 47

Assign each chapter of the book as independent reading. Have students use the Activity Master on page 47 as a study guide to help them identify main ideas and details of each chapter. On the master, students provide supporting details for the main ideas of Chapters 1 and 2. They write both the main idea and details for Chapter 3. Remind students that to find the main idea, they should ask, *What is this chapter all about?* They might turn each main idea statement into a question and then read to find details to answer the question.

Strategy Tip: Self-question

Remind students to ask themselves questions as they read, especially if they are having difficulty understanding the text. For example, they might ask:

Do I understand what this book is mostly about?

Can I identify the states of matter?

Can I explain how properties of matter can be measured?

Can I explain the difference between molecules and atoms?

How are chemical changes different from physical changes?

 Meeting Individual Needs

For specific strategies on meeting individual needs, see pages 90–95.

After Reading

Responding

Initiate a class discussion to assess reading comprehension. Ask:

What is matter? (See pages 5–7 in the student book.) **(identify main idea and details)**

What are the four states of matter? Give an example of each. (See pages 8–9.) **(compare and contrast)**

Why do scientists measure matter? (See page 10.) **(summarize)**

What does density measure? (See page 12.) **(summarize)**

How are elements, atoms, and molecules related? (See pages 16–17.) **(compare and contrast)**

Give examples of chemical and physical changes. How are these changes different from a nuclear reaction? (See pages 24–25.) **(summarize)**

Why do scientists conduct experiments? (See pages 26–27.) **(draw conclusions)**

 Writing and Research: Write a Report

Activity Master, Page 48

Students can choose one scientist from the student book and write a report describing his or her life and contributions.

Communicating: Viewing

Analyze an image

Have students choose an image from the student book that relates to the content of their reports. Ask:

What is the message or main idea of the image you've chosen? What details help explain this message?

How does the person described in your report relate to the image you've chosen?

What title would you give this image?

Students should

✓ state main ideas and details of the image

✓ respond to the message in an image

✓ relate the topic of their scientist reports to their images

Extend and Assess

Focus on Science

Thinking Like a Scientist

Process Skill: Experimenting

Answers for page 27: 1. and 2. Student answers should match information shown on page 27. 3. Five 4. The data supports her conclusion.

Check It Out: Salt helps make roads less icy. Ice with salt. Student answers will vary.

Experimenting
Activity Master, Page 49

Students use the Activity Master to choose a hypothesis and decide how they would conduct an experiment to test the hypothesis. While students will only plan the experiment for this activity, you might want them to actually conduct it if time permits and materials are available.

Hands-on Science

Summary Students change matter from a liquid state to a solid state.

Tips Have students make sure all lids are closed tightly. Remind students to include the salt. The experiment will not work properly without the salt.

Safety Note Survey students for food allergies. If you approve, students without allergies may eat the ice cream. Students should clean up spills immediately to avoid slipping.

Answers to Think *At the beginning of the experiment, the matter was in a liquid state. At the end, the matter is in a solid state. A physical change took place. The milk and syrup have changed states, not chemical properties.*

Assessment Options

Use the following assessment options to assess students' understanding of *Matter, Matter Everywhere.*

Questions

Use the following questions during individual conferences or ask students to write the answers in their notebooks:

1 What is one example of each state of matter?

2 Explain the difference between a chemical change and a physical change. Provide an example of each.

3 What are some properties of gold?

4 Are most of the things in the world made up of compounds? Explain.

5 Why is a hypothesis important to an experiment?

Assessment Activity

Ask students to create a diagram that shows the relationship between matter, compounds, and elements. Students should include labels and captions to communicate their ideas. Students can use *Matter, Matter Everywhere* and other resources to complete their diagrams.

Diagrams should

✓ clearly represent the relationship between all topics listed

✓ be well-organized and carefully prepared

✓ include a title

✓ use correct grammar and mechanics

Multiple-Choice Test

Use the multiple-choice test on page 110.

Cross-Curricular Connection

Mathematics

Have students use the time line on pages 20–21 in the student book to figure out how many years have passed between the discovery of strontium and aluminum (35 years) and neon and americium (47 years).

Home-School Connection

Students can explain to parents the difference between chemical and physical changes in matter. Then students and parents can predict which type of change is most common in their own homes. They can observe changes to matter in their homes over the course of one day, identifying each change as either physical or chemical. Then they can discuss whether or not their prediction was correct.

Vocabulary: Relate Words

The words below are from *Matter, Matter Everywhere*. Each word has something to do with what matter is or how matter is measured. Use the glossary of the student book to check your understanding of each word. Then write a sentence for each word that shows how you think it relates to matter.

Word	Meaning	My Sentence
atom		
chemistry		
gas		
liquid		
mass		
state		
volume		

Reading: Identify Main Idea and Details

The main idea of a chapter is what the chapter is mostly about. Details are facts and examples that explain more about the main idea. Finish the chart with details and main ideas.

Chapter 1   **Main Idea:** *Matter has properties and exists in different states.*

Details

-
-
-
-

Chapter 2   **Main Idea:** *All matter is made of atoms arranged in various ways.*

Details

-
-
-
-

Chapter 3   **Main Idea:**

Details

-
-
-
-

Writing: Prewriting

Write a Report

You will be writing a report on one scientist from *Matter, Matter Everywhere*. Whom will you choose? Organize your ideas before you write.

My Scientist: _____

I. Childhood and education

    A. _____

    B. _____

II. What scientist was trying to prove

    A. _____

    B. _____

III. Scientists who influenced this person's work

    A. _____

    B. _____

IV. Why this scientist's work is important

    A. _____

    B. _____

My sources:

_____

_____

_____

Thinking Like a Scientist: Experimenting

Scientists conduct experiments to test an idea or hypothesis. Use the hypothesis provided below or write your own hypothesis. Then complete this page to design an experiment that will test the hypothesis.

Hypothesis: The volume of a large marble is more than the volume of a pair of scissors.

1. List materials you will need for your experiment.

_____

_____

_____

2. Describe each step of the experiment.

Step 1: _____

_____

Step 2: _____

_____

Step 3: _____

_____

Step 4: _____

_____

3. Predict what you think the results of the experiment will be.

_____

_____

4. How can you share or communicate your results?

_____

5. On the back of this page, sketch what your experiment will look like when it is set up.

Newton's Laws

By Glen Phelan

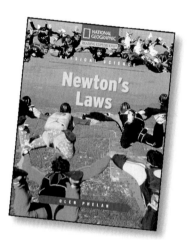

Summary

A jet flying overhead, a javelin sailing through the air, a roller coaster looping upside-down—these and all other movements are explained by Newton's three laws of motion. Isaac Newton developed these laws in the 1600s as he built upon the work of earlier scientists such as Galileo. The first law states that an object will remain at rest or continue moving at the same speed in the same direction unless a force acts on it. The second law links force and mass to acceleration. The third law explains that, for every action, there is an equal and opposite reaction. Although Isaac Newton developed his laws hundreds of years ago, scientists and engineers today still rely on these laws to make things move faster and more easily.

Science Background

Many people consider Isaac Newton the greatest scientist who ever lived. His discoveries about motion and gravity became the basis for explaining how the universe works. Not only did he make an extraordinary number of important discoveries, but he used math to prove his ideas. His work set the stage for many modern developments in science, yet he was very humble about his greatness. He once said, "[T]o myself I seem to have been only like a boy playing on the seashore, and diverting myself in now and then finding a smoother pebble or a prettier shell than ordinary, whilst the great ocean of truth lay all undiscovered before me."

Learning Objectives

Science

- Explain Newton's first, second, and third laws of motion
- Give examples of how Newton's laws of motion explain the movements of everyday objects
- Identify some of Galileo's and Newton's characteristics that helped them in their scientific work
- Describe some of Newton's scientific discoveries and accomplishments
- Explore how Newton's laws of motion affected the development of flight

Process Skills

Skill Focus
- Predicting

Supporting Skills
- Inferring
- Defining operationally
- Hypothesizing

Reading Skills

Genre: Expository

Skill Focus
- Identify cause-and-effect relationships
- Use specialized words

Supporting Skills
- Identify main ideas and details
- Summarize

Focus on Reading

Before Reading

Activate Prior Knowledge

Do a simple demonstration to introduce motion. Roll a ball across the floor so that it bumps into a wall. After the ball comes to a stop, ask: *Why does the ball start rolling?* (You pushed it.) *Why does the ball stop?* If students say it bumps into the wall, roll the ball down a hallway or roll the ball in the class more slowly so that it stops before hitting the wall. Again ask: *Why does the ball stop?* Record all responses on the board to revisit later. Some students may correctly say that friction with the floor makes the ball stop. Explain that they will find out more about motion and forces as they read this book.

Preview

Lead students as they preview the book. Draw their attention to chapter titles, photos, section titles, sidebars, and other special features. Ask:

What do the chapter titles tell you about the contents of this book?

Skim the first chapter to find the blue questions. Can you answer these questions now? Do you think you'll be able to answer them after reading the chapter?

Look at the photos in Chapter 2. When do you think Isaac Newton lived? What are some things he investigated?

Set Purpose

Ask students whether this book reminds them of other books they have read. Help students set a purpose for reading. Ask:

What do you want to find out about Isaac Newton and his laws of motion?

Encourage students to give reasons for their answers. Model your own purpose for reading, such as *I want to read to find out how Newton made his discoveries.*

Vocabulary Strategy: Use Specialized Words

Activity Master, Page 54

Ask students to put these words in a category: ball, bat, pitcher, catcher, home run. Students will likely identify that all these words are about baseball. Explain that some words are used to describe a specific topic or process. These specialized words can be grouped together because their meanings are related in some way. The words on the Activity Master on page 54 all have something to do with motion. As students read the book, they can use the glossary to help them write how each word relates to motion. Students will use the following words:

acceleration
force
friction
inertia
mass
reaction force

Correlation to National Standards

Writing Skills

Writing Focus
• Write an introduction (descriptive)

Supporting Skills
• Use the writing process
• Create an outline
• Respond to others' writing

Speaking/Listening
• Present an introduction

Science

• Scientific inquiry (K–4, 5–8)
• Motions and forces (5–8)
• Position and motion of objects (K–4)
• Abilities of technological design (K–4, 5–8)
• Understanding about science and technology (K–4, 5–8)
• Transfer of energy (5–8)
• History of science (5–8)

Reading/Language Arts

• Read to acquire information about Isaac Newton's three laws of motion
• Apply a wide range of strategies, such as identifying causes and effects, to comprehend text
• Use a variety of informational resources to gather information and communicate knowledge
• Use spoken language to exchange information

During Reading

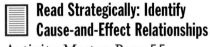 **Read Strategically: Identify Cause-and-Effect Relationships**

Activity Master, Page 55

Assign each chapter of the book as independent reading. Have students use the Activity Master on page 55 to help them identify causes and effects. Remind students that the effect is what happened. The cause is why it happened. Students identify causes and effects to better understand Newton's laws and how they affect the motion of objects.

Strategy Tip: Take notes

If students have difficulty remembering the information in the book, encourage them to take notes. Remind students that notes should be brief, highlighting the most important ideas. You might show different types of notes, such as lists, webs, and outlines. Students could use the chapter and section titles as headings for their notes.

Meeting Individual Needs

For specific strategies on meeting individual needs, see pages 90–95.

After Reading

Responding

Initiate a class discussion to assess reading comprehension. Ask:

A ship slows down when it hits a wave. A soccer ball stops when it hits the net. What is happening in each case? (See pages 7–9 in the student book.) **(identify main idea and details)**

Summarize Newton's second law of motion. (See pages 10–11.) **(summarize)**

Give examples of how you have used each of Newton's laws in your movements so far today. (See pages 7–14.) **(make judgments)**

What are some of Isaac Newton's most important discoveries? (See pages 9, 11, 12, and 19.) **(summarize)**

What qualities of Newton made him a good scientist? (See pages 15–17.) **(make judgments)**

How have Newton's discoveries helped in the exploration and use of space? (See pages 20–25.) **(identify cause-and-effect relationships)**

Writing and Research: Write an Introduction

Activity Master, Page 56

Draw students' attention to Chapter 2. This chapter highlights some important events in Isaac Newton's life and tells about some of his most important discoveries. Ask students to imagine that they work in a science museum. They are planning an exhibit about a famous scientist. On the Activity Master on page 64, students choose a scientist and write an introduction for the exhibit. Their introductions should mention important facts about the scientists' lives as well as their discoveries and accomplishments. Students will use the Activity Master to organize information for their introductions.

Communicating: Speaking/Listening

Present an introduction

Encourage students to organize their introductions in outline form on index cards. They can then deliver their introductions as if they were at the opening of the museum. Remind students that some of their listeners may not know anything about these scientists.

Students reading aloud should

✓ speak clearly and with expression
✓ make eye contact with listeners
✓ provide information about the scientist

Listeners should

✓ listen politely
✓ ask questions to clarify

Extend and Assess

Focus on Science

Thinking Like a Scientist

Process Skill: Predicting

Answer for page 11: The distances thrown would increase.

Answers for page 27: 1. The ball will travel straight, as Newton's first law predicts, because the pulling force of the athlete no longer exists. 2. No, the ball will go straight in the direction of the force.

Check It Out: Possible response: If she pushes the backpack away from the direction of the shuttle, the backpack will push with equal force in the opposite direction and send her moving towards the shuttle.

 Predicting
Activity Master, Page 57

Students use what they know about Newton's laws of motion to predict what will happen in certain situations.

Hands-on Science

Summary Students use simple materials to show Newton's laws of motion in action. Students place an index card and a coin on top of a plastic cup. They observe what happens when they flick the card with varying amounts of force. Then students twirl a tennis ball taped to a string. They predict and observe how the ball moves when released.

Tips The ball should be twirled about an inch above the ground so that it rolls instead of bounces when released. This will make it easier for students to see the path of the ball.

Safety Notes Be sure that the tennis balls are taped securely to the strings. There should be enough room so that twirling balls do not hit one another. You might do this activity outside on a hard surface.

Answers to Think *First law: In the coin drop, the flicking force acted on the card, not the coin. The coin's inertia kept it in place over the cup, allowing it to drop in the cup. In the ball twirl, once the pulling force was removed from the ball, it no longer kept its circular motion. It moved away in a straight line. Second law: The strength of the force you apply to the card or the ball affect how much these objects accelerate.*

Assessment Options

Use the following assessment options to assess students' understanding of *Newton's Laws.*

Questions

Use the following questions during individual conferences or ask students to write the answers independently in their notebooks:

1 Give an example of how Newton's laws of motion affect your life.

2 How is force related to mass and acceleration?

3 Give an example of action and reaction forces.

4 Name two discoveries Newton made.

5 Name three ways modern technology relies on the work of Isaac Newton.

Assessment Activity

Have students create picture albums that show Newton's laws. They should have one section for each law. They can get pictures from newspapers, magazines, the Internet, or draw their own.

Picture albums should

✓ include at least three pictures that show each law of motion
✓ contain pictures that are correctly categorized
✓ be neat and organized

Multiple-Choice Test

Use the multiple-choice test on page 111.

Cross-Curricular Connection

Physical Education

Students can devise a game that illustrates one or more of Newton's laws. Have them write the rules of the game, tell how the game illustrates the law, and demonstrate the game for the class. Alternatively, students can choose a sport and demonstrate how it illustrates Newton's laws. They can draw diagrams to explain the laws.

Home-School Connection

Ask students to summarize Newton's laws of motion for their families. Then students can work with their family members to think of an example of each law from their daily lives. Allow time for students to share their examples with the class.

Vocabulary: Use Specialized Words

The words below are from *Newton's Laws*. Each word has something to do with motion. Write the meaning of each word. Use *Newton's Laws* and its glossary to help you. Then write a sentence to explain how the word relates to motion.

Word	Meaning	My Sentence
acceleration		
force		
friction		
inertia		
mass		
reaction force		

Reading: Identify Cause-and-Effect Relationships

As you read *Newton's Laws*, think about things that happen and why those things happen. Complete the chart by finding the effect of each cause or the cause of each effect.

Cause

Effect

Two objects push against each other.	→	
	→	The force of an object increases.
Two hockey pucks slide across the ice and collide.	→	
A rocket burns fuel and produces hot gases.	→	
	→	A ball hit into the air falls to the ground.

Reading Strategies

Writing: Use the Writing Process

Write an Introduction

Newton's Laws tells about Isaac Newton's life and some important discoveries he made. The book also mentions other important scientists, such as Edmund Halley and Galileo Galilei.

You are planning a new exhibit at a science museum. Your exhibit tells about a scientist and his or her discoveries. Your job is to find important information for the introduction to the exhibit.

1. **Choose a scientist.** My scientist: _____

2. **Do research.** Use reference sources to find out more about your scientist. You could use the Internet, encyclopedias, biographies, or articles in magazines. List major ideas in the table below.

Facts About the Scientist's Life	Facts About the Scientist's Discoveries

3. **Create an outline.** Look at the most important facts and create an outline for your introduction. Write your ideas on index cards.

   ✓ Do not write your introduction word for word. Instead, list on each card a few facts or ideas to guide you while you speak.

   ✓ Put your cards in an order that makes sense. Number each card in case you drop them.

4. **Practice your introduction.** Present your introduction to a partner or small group of classmates. Use your cards, but remember to look up at your classmates. Speak clearly and with enthusiasm.

Thinking Like a Scientist: Predicting

Use what you know about Newton's laws of motion to answer the questions below.

1. One soccer ball rolls across a smooth parking lot, and another rolls across grass. Which soccer ball will roll the greater distance? Explain why.

   _____

   _____

   _____

2. You throw two baseballs. You throw one against the wind, and the other with the wind. Which ball will travel farther? Explain why.

   _____

   _____

   _____

3. You are going to throw a baseball and a bowling ball with the same amount of force. Which ball will travel the least distance? Which of Newton's laws helps you predict the answer?

   _____

   _____

4. You are playing tetherball. You are hitting the ball in a circular motion when the ball comes loose from the string. What will happen to the ball? How do you know?

   _____

   _____

5. Brenda pulls a wagon that is loaded with a bag of empty aluminum cans. Joe pulls a wagon that is loaded with newspapers and magazines. Who needs to pull with more force—Brenda or Joe? Explain why.

   _____

   _____

   _____

The Magic of Light and Sound

By Rebecca L. Johnson

Summary

We experience the world largely through sight and hearing, our two senses that respond to light and sound. Both these forms of energy travel in waves that can differ in wavelength and frequency. While light waves can move through a vacuum, sound waves can travel only by causing particles of matter—gases, liquids, and solids—to vibrate. Both light and sound waves reflect off hard, flat surfaces. For sound waves, this reflection is called an echo. We put light and sound waves to work in many ways. Contact lenses, cameras, and telescopes all bend light. Sonar and ultrasound scans use sound waves. Lasers are used for many things, from surgeons' scalpels to fiber optics.

Science Background

Waves of light and sound give us much of our information about the world around us. But seeing and hearing don't happen in the eyes and ears. These sense organs just gather light and sound for the brain to decode into images and sounds. The process of seeing starts when light waves come into the eye through the pupil and travel through the lens, which focuses light on the retina. The retina changes information about light into nerve signals the brain can understand. Hearing starts when sound waves travel into the ear and cause the eardrum and tiny bones in the ear to vibrate. In the inner ear, the cochlea changes the sound vibrations into nerve signals the brain can understand. These processes allow us to explore our world in ways that would otherwise be impossible.

Learning Objectives

Science

- Explain how light waves and sound waves travel
- Describe the difference between reflection and refraction of light waves
- Learn how people see light and hear sounds
- Understand that both light and sound waves can reflect off objects
- Recognize that sound waves travel through different materials at different speeds but cannot travel through a vacuum
- Recognize how light and sound technologies are used in scientific investigations and in daily life

Process Skills

Skill Focus
- Defining operationally

Supporting Skills
- Observing
- Communicating
- Collecting data
- Inferring

Reading Skills

Genre: Expository

Skill Focus
- Draw conclusions
- Use prefixes

Supporting Skills
- Recognize cause-and-effect relationships
- Compare and contrast
- Reread

Focus on Reading

Before Reading

Activate Prior Knowledge

Ask students to think about light and sound in their lives. You might ask questions, such as these:

How do you use light and sound for learning? For entertainment?

What are some ways sound and light are used for safety?

Write students' ideas in a chart on the board (see below). Have students copy the chart into their notebooks and complete each column with partners. Explain that the book they are about to read tells about how light and sound help people experience the world.

Light	Sound
read books	hear music
see movies	hear movies
street lights	siren

Preview

Give students time to flip through the book, paying attention to chapter titles, photos, captions, and diagrams. Ask:

From reading chapter titles, can you predict what this book will be about?

Why are some images in the book black and white?

Look at the diagrams on pages 8 and 20. What does each diagram show?

Set Purpose

Ask students whether this book reminds them of other books they have read. Help them set a purpose for reading. Ask:

What do you want to find out by reading this book?

Vocabulary Strategy: Use Prefixes

Activity Master, Page 62

Explain to students that the meanings for many words in the English language can be figured out using the meaning of the word's prefix. For example, the word *preview* has the prefix *pre-*, which means "at an earlier time." Ask students to suggest a definition for *preview*. Then have them check their ideas in a dictionary. (*Preview* means "an early or advance view, for example, of a movie or play.") Students can use the Activity Master on page 62 to write a definition for each vocabulary word based on the meaning of its prefix. Students will use these words:

- bioluminescence
- infrasounds
- reflect
- refraction
- ultrasound
- ultraviolet light

Correlation to National Standards

Writing Skills	Science	Reading/Language Arts
Writing Focus • Write a report (expository) **Supporting Skills** • Use the writing process • Use an outline • Conduct research **Viewing** • Create a diagram	• Light, heat, electricity, and magnetism (K–4) • Transfer of energy (5–8) • Science and technology (K–4, 5–8) • Science as a human endeavor (K–4, 5–8) • Scientific inquiry (K–4, 5–8) • Nature of science (K–4, 5–8)	• Read to be informed and to build an understanding of the physical world • Apply a wide range of strategies to comprehend and interpret texts • Use and adjust visual and written language to communicate effectively • Use the writing process • Conduct research • Use a variety of informational resources

During Reading

**Read Strategically:
Draw Conclusions**

Activity Master, Page 63

Assign each chapter of the book as independent reading. As students read, they can use the Activity Master on page 63 to draw conclusions about light and sound. Explain that readers draw conclusions about people and events using facts and details they read and what they already know. Model drawing conclusions using the first set of facts and details. (See answers below for Activity Master on page 63.)

Strategy Tip: Reread

Remind students to reread sections they are having difficulty understanding. They might read ahead a section or two and then reread the section they are having trouble with to help clarify understanding. Encourage students to discuss problematic sections during the follow-up discussion.

**Meeting
Individual Needs**

For specific strategies on meeting individual needs, see pages 90–95.

After Reading

Responding

Initiate a class discussion to assess reading comprehension. Ask:

What do waves and vibrations have to do with hearing sound? (See pages 7–11 in the student book.) **(identify cause-and-effect relationships)**

What is the difference between infrasounds and ultrasound? (See page 8.) **(compare and contrast)**

What are examples of light being reflected, refracted, and absorbed? (See page 13.) **(identify cause-and-effect relationships)**

What is the difference between visible light and ultraviolet light? (See page 15.) **(compare and contrast)**

How did Newton and Galileo contribute to our understanding of light and sound? (See pages 16 and 19.) **(summarize)**

What are ways people put light and sound to work for them? (See pages 18–23.) **(summarize)**

**Writing and Research:
Write a Report**

Activity Master, Page 64

Have students choose an invention that uses light or sound or both. Ask them to find out about the inventor, describe the invention, and explain how this invention helps people. Students can choose an invention discussed in the student book, or they can choose another invention.

Communicating: Viewing

Create a diagram

Students can create a simple diagram of the invention they write about. Their diagrams should include a title and labels and might include symbols such as arrows. Remind students that their diagrams should be simple and easy to understand.

Diagrams should

✓ include labeled parts

✓ include symbols to show a process

✓ include a title and labels

Facts and Details from the Book	What I Can Conclude
(1) Sound travels in waves in different frequencies. People can hear some sounds but not ultrasounds or infrasounds.	(1) People cannot hear all frequencies of sound.
(2) Sound travels through air and water but not through space. Sound echoes when it bounces off something.	(2) Sound travels through some materials but not others. Sound can bounce back from some materials.
(3) Mirrors reflect light, lenses and prisms refract light, and many objects absorb light.	(3) Light travels in a straight line until it strikes an object. Then it changes.
(4) People have invented telescopes, movies, lenses, CD players, medical and navigation equipment, fiber optic cables, and lasers.	(4) People use inventions for light and sound to help them understand and enjoy the world.
(5) Newton and the prism; Galileo and the telescope	(5) Many scientists have helped us understand light and sound.

Extend and Assess

Focus on Science

Thinking Like a Scientist

Process Skill: Defining operationally

Answer for page 16: A mirror is a piece of glass that reflects, or bounces back, light waves. A mirror does not give off its own light.

Answers for pages 26–27: 1. The water glass showed a rainbow on the wall; when the glass was picked up, the rainbow disappeared. 2. It was refracted. 3. prism, rain 4. A prism is an object that refracts, or bends, light waves to form a rainbow, or spectrum.

Answer for Check It Out: No, because the light would have to have been refracted through some other object.

Defining Operationally

Activity Master, Page 65

Students use the Activity Master to write an operational definition for an object they choose. They then describe how the object uses light waves or sound waves.

Hands-on Science

Summary Students set up an experiment to find out how far a sound will travel. A pin, a ruler, and a table are some of the materials students use to listen to a pin drop at varying distances.

Tips Have students recheck their measurements using the meter stick. Also, students dropping the pin might want to alert the listener each time before actually dropping the pin. This will prepare listeners for listening.

Answers to Think *Some surfaces, such as cloth, would absorb some of the vibrations caused by the pin dropping, so not as much sound would be produced. Other surfaces, such as a metal pan, would vibrate more when the pin is dropped, so more sound waves would be produced.*

Assessment Options

Use the following assessment options to assess students' understanding.

Questions

Use the following questions during individual conferences or ask students to write the answers in their notebooks:

1 Compare how light waves and sound waves travel.

2 Give one example each of light reflecting, refracting, and being absorbed.

3 How do people hear sound and see light?

4 Why can't people hear ultrasounds or see ultraviolet light?

5 What are three inventions that help people use light or sound to understand the world?

Assessment Activity

Students create an illustrated dictionary of five important people, inventions, or terms from *The Magic of Light and Sound*. Students can use pictures from magazines or they can draw pictures.

Dictionaries should

✓ include at least five entries with matching text and images

✓ use alphabetical order

✓ be accurate

✓ be carefully prepared

✓ use correct grammar and mechanics

Multiple-Choice Test

Use the multiple-choice test on page 112.

Cross-Curricular Connection

Literature

Students read age-appropriate science fiction books or short stories. They can read to see how the principles of light or sound are applied to devices or inventions in the book. Students can then compare these science fiction devices to devices that exist today.

Home-School Connection

Students and family members can rent a video about light and sound (or read together a nonfiction book about this topic, for example, Dorling Kindersley's *Light*.) Ask students to talk about how the information is presented compared to the student book. Is one source more detailed than the other? Does each source use similar examples?

Vocabulary: Use Prefixes to Understand Words

Many words in the English language have prefixes. The meanings of some of these words can be figured out if you know the meanings of the prefixes.

The words below all have prefixes. Use the meaning of each prefix to write a definition for each vocabulary word. Then check your definition using the glossary and write any new information about the word in the third column.

bio-	life or something living	*re-*	to go back or go again
infra-	below or beneath	*ultra-*	to go beyond or outside of

Word	Using Prefix Definition	Glossary Definition
bioluminescence		
infrasounds		
reflect		
refraction		
ultrasound		
ultraviolet light		

Reading: Draw Conclusions

You draw a conclusion by putting facts and details together with what you already know. Complete the chart by adding facts and details or conclusions you can draw.

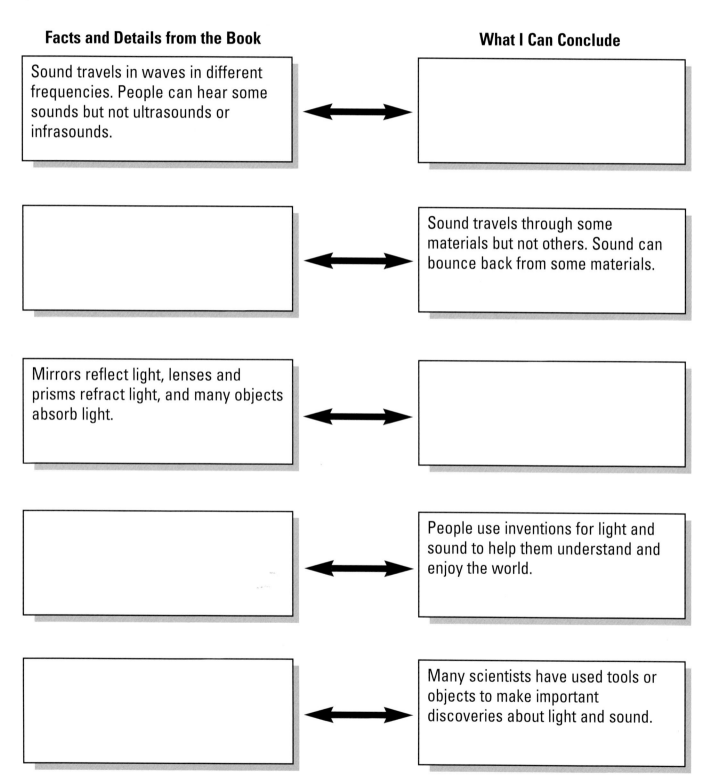

Facts and Details from the Book   **What I Can Conclude**

Sound travels in waves in different frequencies. People can hear some sounds but not ultrasounds or infrasounds.

Sound travels through some materials but not others. Sound can bounce back from some materials.

Mirrors reflect light, lenses and prisms refract light, and many objects absorb light.

People use inventions for light and sound to help them understand and enjoy the world.

Many scientists have used tools or objects to make important discoveries about light and sound.

Writing: Use the Writing Process

Write a Report

You will write a report about an invention that uses light, sound, or both. You can write your report on an invention from the student book, or you can find an invention on your own. Use the outline to organize your ideas for your report.

The invention is _____

I. Name and information about the inventor

    A. _____

    B. _____

II. Ways this invention helps people

    A. _____

    B. _____

III. How this invention uses light, sound, or both, in simple terms
(Include a simple sketch on the back of this page.)

    A. _____

    B. _____

IV. Who benefits most from this invention, or who uses it most often

    A. _____

    B. _____

Use your outline to write a report on a separate sheet of paper.

Name _____

Thinking Like a Scientist: Defining Operationally

Scientists use their observations and experiences to describe how an object functions. To write an operational definition, choose one object in the list or another object that uses light and sound. Then answer the questions below.

List of Topics: Choose One	**Other Ideas:**
drum	_____
hearing aid	_____
microscope	_____
telescope	
sonar	

Topic you choose _____

Write an operational definition for your topic. An operational definition is a description of the object based on what it does or how it works.

_____

_____

_____

How does your topic use light waves or sound waves?
Draw a simple sketch to help you explain.

_____

_____

Science Skills

The Mystery of Magnets

By Pamela Bliss

Summary

Magnets have a mysterious, invisible force that people have tried to understand for centuries. *The Mystery of Magnets* explores how magnets attract and repel each other. Students will learn how magnetism relates to Earth and certain animal behaviors. Magnets are found in nature and people have learned to use magnets and magnetism in many different ways to make their lives easier. Magnetic force can be combined with electricity to create temporary magnets that provide electricity. Magnets help doctors to study how the human body and brain work and are used in a wide variety of fields and applications.

Science Background

Earth has an enormous magnetic field, just as a small bar magnet has a small magnetic field. So Earth acts like a huge magnet. Like any magnet, Earth has magnetic north and south poles. That's why a compass works. The poles of the magnetized needle on a compass align with Earth's magnetic field. So the north pole of the needle always points to Earth's magnetic north pole. But this is not the same as the geographic North Pole. Over time, Earth's magnetic poles move, but the geographic poles do not. Currently, the magnetic north pole is in northern Canada, about 1,250 km (775 miles) from the geographic North Pole.

Learning Objectives

Science

- Describe how magnets act on objects and other magnets
- Explain how Earth is a magnet
- Identify discoveries that people have made throughout history about magnetism
- Explore the relationship between electricity and magnetism
- Understand how people continue to use magnets to solve problems

Process Skills

Skill Focus
- Inferring

Supporting Skills
- Communicating
- Observing
- Interpreting data

Reading Skills

Genre: Expository

Skill Focus
- Identify main idea and details
- Relate words

Supporting Skills
- Make generalizations
- Summarize
- Identify cause-and-effect relationships

Focus on Reading

Before Reading

Activate Prior Knowledge

Have students look at the cover of the book and then ask them to think about what they know about magnets. Ask:

What is a magnet? What does it do?

How can you use magnets?

Write students' ideas on a K-W-L chart. Explain that in the first column, students will write what they know about magnets and magnetism. In the second column, they will write what they want to know or questions they have about magnets and magnetism.

Have students copy the K-W-L chart into their notebooks and complete the first two columns with partners. They can return to the chart after reading to identify what they learned and what they still want to find out.

Preview

Give students time to preview the book, paying attention to chapter titles, photos, captions, and special features. Ask:

What information is shown in the photos?

What do the headings tell you about the topics covered in this book?

Set Purpose

Ask students whether this book reminds them of other books they have read. Ask:

What do you want to find out by reading this book?

Vocabulary Strategy: Relate Words

Activity Master, Page 70

Have students read the title of the book, *The Mystery of Magnets*. Explain to students that the vocabulary words they will be learning all relate in some way to magnets and magnetism. Students can use the glossary to find the meaning of each word. They then write a sentence telling how each word relates to magnets and magnetism. Students will be using these words:

attract
compass
electromagnet
magnetic field
pole
repel

What I Know	What I Want To Know	What I Learned

Correlation to National Standards

Writing Skills

Writing Focus
• Write a report (expository)

Supporting Skills
• Use the writing process
• Use an outline
• Conduct research

Speaking/Listening
• Give an oral presentation

Science

• Scientific inquiry (K–4, 5–8)
• Light, heat, electricity, and magnetism (K–4)
• Science and technology in local challenges (K–4, 5–8)
• Science as a human endeavor (K–4, 5–8)
• Properties of objects and materials (K–4)

Reading/Language Arts

• Read to understand magnets and their importance in our world
• Apply a wide range of strategies to comprehend and interpret texts
• Use visual and written language to communicate
• Conduct research
• Use the writing process

During Reading

 Read Strategically: Identify Main Idea and Details

Activity Master, Page 71

Assign each chapter of the book as independent reading. Have students use the Activity Master on page 71 as a study guide to help them identify main ideas and details of each chapter. On the Activity Master, students provide supporting details for the main ideas of Chapters 1 and 2. They write the main idea and supporting details for Chapter 3. Remind students that to find the main idea, they should ask themselves what the chapter is mostly about. They might then turn each main idea into a question and read to find details to answer the question.

Strategy Tip: Paraphrase

Suggest that students restate in their own words any passages—from sentences to entire paragraphs—they would like to clarify for themselves. The process of paraphrasing requires students to identify the important ideas in the passages and summarize them. If students are still having difficulty restating a particular passage, they can ask for clarification during the follow-up class discussion.

 Meeting Individual Needs

For specific strategies on meeting individual needs, see page 90–95.

After Reading

Responding

Initiate a class discussion to assess reading comprehension. Ask:

What are some of the ways we use magnets every day? (See pages 12, 19, and 22–25 in the student book.) **(make generalizations)**

How does a magnet work? (See pages 6–13.) **(summarize)**

Where are some places magnets occur in nature? (See pages 4–5, 12–13, and 14–15.) **(summarize)**

What effect does electricity have on a magnetic field? (See pages 18–19.) **(identify cause-and-effect relationships)**

What tools have scientists used to better understand magnets and magnetism? (Answers will vary.) **(draw conclusions)**

 Writing and Research: Write a Report

Activity Master, Page 72

Students can choose an invention that uses magnets to help people do work. Have students find out about the inventor, describe the invention, and explain how this invention helps people. Students can choose an invention discussed in the book or they can choose a different invention. Use the Activity Master on page 72 to help students plan their report.

Communicating: Speaking/Listening

Give an oral presentation

In small groups, students can read their reports aloud.

Students reading aloud should

✓ speak clearly
✓ make eye contact with listeners
✓ use emphasis as appropriate

Listeners should

✓ listen politely
✓ determine the main points of the report
✓ ask questions to clarify

Extend and Assess

Focus on Science

Thinking Like a Scientist

Process Skill: Inferring

Answers for page 9: The metal objects (the wire hanger, scissors, can opener, and soft-drink can) would likely be magnetic.

Answers for pages 26: Magnet B is stronger because it attracted the paper clip to itself.

Check It Out: The magnetic force of magnet A is strong enough to attract through the index card.

Inferring

Activity Master, Page 73 Students can use the Activity Master on page 73 to practice making inferences. Remind students that when they infer, they look at the evidence and use what they already know to make a good guess about something.

Hands-on Science

Summary Students use a few simple materials to create a temporary and a permanent magnet.

Tips Have students take special care to stroke the nail on the magnet in the same direction on only one end of the magnet to magnetize it. If they stroke back and forth, the nail will not magnetize.

Answers to Think If you stroked the nail only five times, its magnetic force would be weaker. If you stroked it 40 times, the magnetic force would be stronger; Yes, the strength of the magnet would be affected.

Assessment Options

Use the following assessment options to assess students' understanding of *The Mystery of Magnets.*

Questions

Use the following questions during individual conferences or ask students to write the answers in their notebooks:

1 Name two ways magnets are used every day.

2 Explain how an electromagnet works.

3 What are two places where magnets occur in nature?

4 Explain the magnetic attraction between the north and south poles of a magnet.

5 What are three ways scientists learned about magnetism?

Assessment Activity

Students can create a magnet book. Have students choose four main ideas about magnets and provide details to support their choices. Students can use diagrams or sketches to explain ideas.

Books should
✓ clearly address four important topics
✓ use correct grammar and mechanics
✓ include simple illustrations

Multiple-Choice Test

Use the multiple-choice test on page 113.

Cross-Curricular Connection

Mathematics

Have students use magnets to attract paper clips from a pile and record the number of paper clips attracted. After repeating this five times, students can find the average number of paper clips the magnet will attract by adding all five numbers and then dividing by 5. Using this information, students can discuss which magnets are stronger and which are weaker.

Home-School Connection

Students and their parents can look for magnets and objects that contain magnets around their home and make a list of different magnets they find. They can discuss how these magnets help people do work or make people's lives easier.

Vocabulary: Relate Words

The words below are from *The Mystery of Magnets*. Each word is related to magnets and magnetism in some way. In the chart below, write the meaning of each word. Use the glossary to check the meanings. Then write a sentence for each word that shows how it relates to magnets and magnetism.

Word	Meaning	My Sentence
attract		
compass		
electromagnet		
magnetic field		
pole		
repel		

Reading: Identify Main Idea and Details

The main idea of a chapter is what the chapter is mostly about. Details are facts and examples that explain the main idea. Finish the chart below with details and main ideas.

Chapter 1	**Main Idea:** *Magnets are objects that can attract or repel objects without touching them.*

Details

-
-
-
-

Chapter 2	**Main Idea:** *Throughout history, people have discovered new things about magnets.*

Details

-
-
-
-

Chapter 3	**Main Idea:**

Details

-
-
-
-

Writing: Use the Writing Process

Write a Report

You will write a report about an invention that uses magnets to help people do work. You can write your report on an invention from the book or you can find one on your own. Use the outline below to organize your ideas for your report.

The invention I will write about is _____

I. Details about the inventor

   A. _____

   B. _____

II. Ways this invention helps people

   A. _____

   B. _____

III. How this invention uses magnets (Include a simple sketch in the space below or on the back of this page.)

   A. _____

   B. _____

IV. Who benefits most from this invention or who uses it most often

   A. _____

   B. _____

Include other interesting information you found. Write your report on a separate sheet of paper.

Thinking Like a Scientist: Inferring

Scientists infer, or make a good guess, based on evidence and background knowledge about how or why things are the way they are. Then they can do further experiments to see if they inferred correctly. You can infer as scientists do. Read the situations below and infer to explain what is happening.

1. You try to put three pieces of paper up on the refrigerator with one magnet, and all the papers fall down. What can you infer happened?

   _____

   _____

2. You want to connect two magnets together. One magnet has the north pole marked *N* and south pole marked *S*. The other magnet's poles are not marked. How can you infer which end of the unmarked magnet is the north pole?

   _____

   _____

   _____

3. You are filling a backpack to go hiking. As you put a compass into the backpack, the needle of the compass moves as it goes past the magnetic clasp on the backpack. What can you infer about why the compass needle moved?

   _____

   _____

4. You have a metal object placed near a magnet, but the magnet does not attract the metal object. You move the object closer to the magnet, and then the magnet attracts it. What can you infer about the strength of the magnet?

   _____

   _____

   _____

Understanding Electricity

By Stephen M. Tomecek

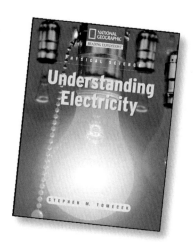

Summary

People around the world depend on electricity in their daily lives. Electricity is a form of energy that is generated by the movement of electrons as they move from atom to atom. Static and current electricity are two types of electricity that are determined by how these electrons move.

Many scientists and inventors have contributed to the development of electric power. Their ideas and systems have led to today's modern power pool. The power pool is a large network of power companies that share resources and supply power to areas where demand is greatest.

Today, almost two-thirds of electric power comes from power plants that burn fossil fuels. Alternative power sources include wind power, solar power, and nuclear power.

Science Background

Since its discovery in the early 1800s, current electricity has revolutionized the way that people live. As our dependency on electricity has grown, so has the demand for electrical power. While we produce huge amounts of electrical power each day, demand often exceeds supply, causing ever more frequent disruptions of power and blackouts. As political leaders and engineers struggle with this dilemma, the future offers hope of new technologies that can help us produce enough electricity without damaging the environment.

Learning Objectives

Science

- Define and give examples of energy
- Describe an electric circuit and its parts
- Recognize that electric circuits can produce light, heat, and magnetic effects
- Define blackouts and explain how people can avoid them

- Recognize that many scientists have contributed to our understanding of electricity
- Identify various resources used for creating electricity

Process Skills

Skill Focus
- Making a model

Supporting Skills
- Observing
- Communicating
- Predicting
- Inferring

Reading Skills

Genre: Expository

Skill Focus
- Make generalizations
- Use specialized words

Supporting Skills
- Identify cause-and-effect relationships
- Summarize
- Use graphic organizers

Before Reading

Activate Prior Knowledge

Ask students what they know about electricity. You might ask questions such as these:

Where does electricity come from?

How does electricity get into our homes?

Write students' ideas in a K-W-L chart on the board. Explain that in the first column, students will write what they know about electricity. In the second column, they will write what they want to know. In the third column, they will write what they have learned after reading the book. Have students copy the K-W-L chart into their notebooks and complete the first two columns with partners. They can return to the chart after reading to complete the third column.

Preview

Give students time to flip through the book and look at chapter titles, photos, captions, and diagrams. Ask:

What topics do you think will be included in this book?

Look at the diagram on pages 20–21. What is the topic of this diagram? What do the numbers help show?

Set Purpose

Ask students whether this book reminds them of other books they have read. Help them set a purpose for reading. Ask:

What do you want to find out by reading this book?

📖 Vocabulary Strategy: Use Specialized Words
Activity Master, Page 78

Explain to students that some words are used to describe a specific or "special" topic, and that these words are called specialized words. Specialized words can be grouped together because their meanings are related. Have students use *Understanding Electricity* and the glossary to help them define each word and then write how each word relates to electricity. Students will use these words:

circuit
conductor
switch
static
volt

What I Know	What I Want To Know	What I Learned

Correlation to National Standards

Writing Skills	Science	Reading/Language Arts
Writing Focus • Write a speech (persuasive) • Use the writing process **Supporting Skills** • Write for a specific audience • Conduct research **Speaking and Listening** • Give an oral presentation	• Light, heat, electricity, and magnetism (K–4) • Transfer of energy (5–8) • Science and technology (K–4, 5–8) • Science as a human endeavor (K–4, 5–8) • Scientific inquiry (K–4, 5–8) • Nature of science (K–4, 5–8) • Types of resources (K–4)	• Apply a wide range of strategies to comprehend and interpret texts • Apply language structure and conventions • Use the writing process • Conduct research • Use language for persuasion • Participate in literacy communities • Use a variety of informational resources

During Reading

 **Read Strategically: Make Generalizations**

Activity Master, Page 79

Assign each chapter of the book as independent reading. As students read, they can write examples that support the generalizations provided on the Activity Master on page 79. Students then write their own generalization about electricity and provide examples to support it.

Remind students that a *generalization* is a kind of conclusion or rule that applies to many examples and use words such as *all, most, many, some, generally,* and *never.*

Strategy Tip: Use graphic organizers

To help students remember the new information in the book, encourage them to create webs to organize details related to main topics, for example, static electricity, currents, and important scientists.

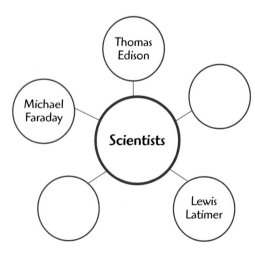

 Meeting Individual Needs

For specific strategies on meeting individual needs, see pages 90–95.

After Reading

Responding

Initiate a class discussion to assess reading comprehension. Ask:

What causes blackouts? (See pages 5 and 15 in the student book.) **(identify cause-and-effect relationships)**

What are important parts of a circuit, and how does a circuit work? (See pages 12–13.) **(summarize)**

Electric circuits can generate heat. What else can electric circuits produce? (See pages 7, 11, and 16.) **(identify cause-and-effect relationships)**

What is the difference between static electricity and current electricity? (See pages 8–10.) **(compare and contrast)**

What are electromagnets? (See pages 10–11.) **(summarize)**

What are some ways to produce electricity? What the benefits and drawbacks for each? (See pages 23–24.) **(identify cause-and-effect relationships)**

Why do people create models? (See pages 26–27.) **(draw conclusions)**

 Writing and Research: Write a Speech

Activity Master, Page 80

Scientists often share their ideas at conferences where they can give and listen to speeches. Students can imagine they are scientists and write a short speech about the best way to produce electricity.

Students should

• identify what they think is the best method to produce electricity

• explain why this method is better than other methods

Suggest that students use *Understanding Electricity* and other resources to research their topic. Students can use the Activity Master on page 80 to help them choose a topic and generate ideas for their speech.

Communicating: Speaking/Listening

Give an oral presentation

Students can present their speeches in small groups.

Students giving speeches should

✓ speak clearly
✓ make eye contact with listeners
✓ adapt speech patterns, such as speak with emphasis on certain points

Listeners should

✓ determine main ideas
✓ ask questions to clarify ideas
✓ listen politely

Extend and Assess

Focus on Science

Thinking Like a Scientist

Process Skill: Making a Model
Answers for page 27: 1. Wire, nail, paper clips, and a battery. 2. Paper clips 3. The model was smaller but both were electromagnets that picked up smaller objects.

Check It Out: Answers will vary, but students might suggest that the wire be wrapped around the nail more than ten times before completing step 3. Students should recognize that only one part of the model should be changed at a time to help them identify possible causes for the changes in the results.

Making a Model
Activity Master, Page 81

Students use the Activity Master to choose a topic and decide how they would build a model of that topic. You might want students to actually build their models if time permits and materials are available.

Hands-on Science

Summary Students create a circuit to model an electrical system. Batteries, insulated wire, and flashlight bulbs help model the process of electricity traveling from a power plant to a home.

Tips If students have trouble lighting the bulbs, have them check their taping to be sure their circuit is properly connected. Also, you might want to draw the model on the board for students to reference.

Safety Notes Make sure students use new batteries. Old batteries could leak or open.

Answers to Think *Students should understand that parallel circuits are a good idea because if one circuit is broken, the rest of the system will still work.*

Assessment Options

Use the following assessment options to assess students' understanding of the book.

Questions
Use the following questions during individual conferences or ask students to write the answers in their notebooks:

1 What is a circuit and how can it be broken?

2 What is one way static electricity is different from current electricity?

3 What are fossil fuels? How are they used to produce electricity?

4 What are two other ways to produce electricity? What are the advantages of each?

5 How does electricity get from a power plant to your home?

Assessment Activity
Students can use magazines and newspapers or create drawings to make posters representing these three concepts from *Understanding Electricity*:

- People depend on electricity.
- Electric circuits can produce light, heat, and magnetic effects.
- There are many ways to produce electricity.

Posters should

✓ clearly address all three concepts
✓ be well-organized and carefully prepared

Multiple-Choice Test
See the multiple-choice test on page 114.

Cross-Curricular Connection

Literature
Ask students to investigate the life of one of the scientists mentioned in *Understanding Electricity*. Students can read age-appropriate biographies or nonfiction books about a scientist and then share some aspect of that person's life and work.

Home-School Connection

Students can discuss with family members how electricity is made and why it's important to conserve energy. Then students and family members can review a household electric bill together. They can identify the amount of electricity the family used in that one month and then together they can identify ways to reduce the amount of electricity they use. Students can then review future bills to see how much energy they are conserving.

Vocabulary: Use Specialized Words

The words below are from *Understanding Electricity*. Each word has something to do with electricity. In each circle, write a meaning for the word. On the lines, write a sentence that shows how the word is related to electricity.

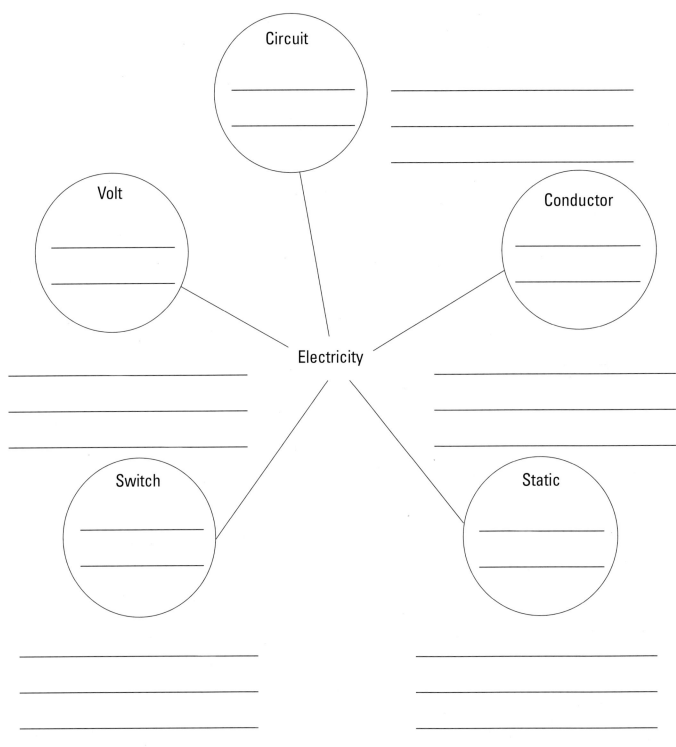

Reading: Make Generalizations

In *Understanding Electricity*, you'll read about how electricity is made and how it is used. Below you will find four generalizations about electricity. Under each generalization, write two or three facts or details from the text that support it. Then, at the bottom of the page, write your own generalization about electricity and provide three examples to support it.

Remember that a generalization is a kind of conclusion or rule that applies to many examples. Generalizations use words such as *all, most, many, some, generally,* and *never.*

All electrical circuits operate in a similar way.

_____

_____

_____

Most of the time, power blackouts don't happen.

_____

_____

_____

Thomas Edison influenced the use of electricity more than any other inventor.

_____

_____

_____

There are many different ways to produce electricity.

_____

_____

_____

Generalization:

Examples:

_____

_____

_____

Writing: Use the Writing Process

Write a Speech

You are a scientist who specializes in how electricity is produced. You will be giving a speech at a conference to share your ideas and suggestions. Choose a topic from the list below or a topic of your own. Keep in mind that you are trying to inform your listeners about your topic and convince them that it is the best way to produce electricity. You will need to use facts and details in your speech, so you might want to conduct research to learn more about your topic. Use the space below to organize your ideas for writing.

List of Topics: Choose One		Other Ideas:
Wind power	Nuclear power	_____
Solar power	Water and fuel cell power	_____
Power from fossil fuels		_____

My topic will be _____

This is how my topic works:

_____

Here are facts that explain why topic should be used:

_____

_____

My topic is better than other options because

_____

_____

Use your ideas to write a speech on a separate sheet of paper.

Thinking Like a Scientist: Making a Model

Scientists create models to test ideas and to learn how things work. Choose a topic from the list below and decide how you can make a model of that topic. Use the space below to plan how you could build the model.

List of Topics: Choose One	**Other Ideas:**
What an atom looks like	_____
What a circuit looks like	_____
How a power pool works	_____
What a power grid system looks like	_____
How electricity gets from the power plant to your home	_____
How fossil fuels are used to make electricity	_____

My topic will be _____

List of parts I will need to show:

_____

Materials I will need and what parts they will represent:

_____

_____

_____

How I will put the parts together (write it out or draw a sketch):

Why this model is useful:

_____

_____

Using Force and Motion

By Glen Phelan

Summary

This book explores the role of force and motion in the world around us. Forces, which are basically pushes or pulls, make things move. Forces also make things slow down, speed up, change direction, or stop. Gravity is a force that affects objects on Earth and in space. Gravity is the pull between two objects. Some forces, such as friction, act on objects to make them slow down or stop. Many scientists have contributed to our understanding of force and motion. Isaac Newton formulated three laws of motion to help explain how objects move. These three laws were built upon ideas developed by Galileo. Today, scientists use their knowledge of force and motion to help people in many ways. For example, the laws of motion can be used to help people travel more efficiently and help athletes improve performance.

Science Background

Isaac Newton, like Galileo Galilei a generation earlier, thought a lot about the nature of motion. Galileo showed that objects of similar size and shape fall at the same speed even if they have different weights. Newton built upon Galileo's work and developed the law of gravity. He also developed three basic laws of motion. Newton's laws of motion explain many principles of force and motion, from how we are able to walk to how planets orbit the sun. Today many scientists and engineers use their understanding of force and motion to improve designs of cars, helmets, and much more to make moving from place to place more efficient.

Learning Objectives

Science

- Explain how the position of an object can be changed by pushing or pulling
- Identify gravity as a force that affects objects on Earth, keeps Earth in orbit around the sun, and keeps the moon, satellites, and other objects in orbit around Earth
- Identify and explain Newton's laws of motion
- Explain how magnets can be used to move objects
- Recognize that many scientists have contributed to our understanding of force and motion

Process Skills

Skill Focus
- Measuring

Supporting Skills
- Observing
- Communicating
- Inferring
- Interpreting data

Reading Skills

Genre: Expository

Skill Focus
- Identify cause-and-effect relationships
- Use context clues

Supporting Skills
- Summarize
- Identify main idea and details
- Paraphrase

Focus on Reading

Before Reading

Activate Prior Knowledge

Direct students' attention to the cover of the student book. Read the title and ask students to describe the content of the photo. Ask:

What objects are moving in the photo?

What makes each object move?

Explain that forces make things move. Forces are pushes or pulls. Explain to students that the book they are about to read discusses how force causes objects to move quickly, slow down, and stop.

Preview

Give students time to flip through the book, paying attention to chapter titles, photos, and captions. Ask:

After looking at photos and reading captions, what topics do you think will be included in this book?

What kinds of information do the sidebars provide?

Look at the diagram on pages 20–21. What does this diagram help explain?

Set Purpose

Ask students whether this book reminds them of other books they have read. Help them set a purpose for reading. Ask:

What do you want to find out by reading this book?

Vocabulary Strategy: Use Context Clues

Activity Master, Page 86

Have students turn to page 10 and read the sentence that contains the word *lubricants*. Then have them read the sentence that comes before and after it. Model for students how to use context clues to figure out word meanings.

Suppose that I have no idea what the word lubricants *means. I can use nearby words and sentences to give me an idea of its meaning. These context clues tell me that examples of lubricants are oil and grease and that lubricants are used in machines. The nearby sentences tell me about how lubricants are slippery and help protect moving parts. I can look up the word in the glossary or in a dictionary to find out more about its meaning, but the context clues have given me a general idea of what* lubricants *means.*

Have students use *Using Force and Motion* to complete the Activity Master on page 86. They will use these words:

air resistance
force
friction
gravity
measure
streamlined

Correlation to National Standards

Writing Skills	Science	Reading/Language Arts
Writing Focus • Write steps in a process (expository) **Supporting Skills** • Prewrite • Conduct research **Speaking/Listening** • Give an oral presentation	• Position and motion of objects (K–4) • Light, heat, electricity, and magnetism (K–4) • Motions and forces (5–8) • Earth in the solar system (5–8) • Science and technology (K–4, 5–8) • Science as a human endeavor (K–4, 5–8) • Scientific inquiry (K–4, 5–8)	• Apply a wide range of strategies to comprehend and interpret texts • Apply language structure and conventions • Use and adjust spoken and written language for learning • Use the writing process • Conduct research • Participate in literacy communities

During Reading

Read Strategically: Identify Cause-and-Effect Relationships

Activity Master, Page 87

Assign each chapter of the book as independent reading. As students read, they can use the Activity Master on page 87 to focus on the cause-and-effect relationships among forces, motion, and objects. To model the process, you might want to work through one example of the chart with the class.

Answers for Activity Master, page 87: 1. A force, such as a push or a pull, makes objects move. 2. Earth's mass is so great that the force of gravity pulls objects towards Earth. (relates to Newton's 1st law of motion) 3. Fiction causes moving objects to slow down and eventually stop. 4. A race car, which has large mass, uses a large force to accelerate quickly. A race car uses a powerful engine to provide the force needed. 5. For every action, there is a reaction. The girl pushes off from the board (action), and the board pushes back on the girl's feet (reaction) and continues to move from the force she exerts on the board. 6. Narrow, smooth shapes create as little air resistance as possible. Air resistance causes objects to slow down.

Strategy Tip: Paraphrase

Suggest that students restate in their own words any passages they would like to clarify for themselves. The process of paraphrasing requires students to identify the important ideas in the passages and summarize them. If students are still having difficulty restating a particular passage, they can ask for clarification during the follow-up class discussion.

Meeting Individual Needs

For specific strategies on meeting individual needs, see pages 90–95.

After Reading

Responding

Initiate a class discussion to assess reading comprehension. Ask:

What makes an object move? Provide an example. (See page 7 in the student book.) **(identify cause-and-effect relationships)**

How does gravity affect objects on Earth and in space? Why? (See pages 8–9.) **(identify cause-and-effect relationships)**

How did Galileo change the way people thought about force and motion? (See page 13.) **(summarize)**

What are Newton's three laws of motion? (See pages 14–19.) **(identify main idea and details)**

How are magnets used to move trains? (See page 23.) **(identify cause-and-effect relationships)**

Why are some cars and trains built with streamlined shapes? (See pages 22–25.) **(identify cause-and-effect relationships)**

Writing and Research: Write Steps in a Process

Activity Master, Page 88

Scientists and sports trainers often use knowledge about force and motion to improve an athlete's performance.

Students can choose a sport and write five steps explaining how to execute that sport. They can conduct research on the sport to learn how coaches help players improve performance. When students have completed the steps in the process, they should then identify how force and laws of motion apply to each step. Students can use the Activity Master on page 88 to help them organize their ideas.

Communicating: Speaking/Listening

Give an oral presentation
Students can read aloud their steps in a process in groups.

Students reading aloud should

✓ speak clearly

✓ make eye contact with listeners

✓ adapt speech patterns, such as pause after reading each step

Listeners should

✓ determine main ideas

✓ identify how force and laws of motion apply to each step

✓ ask questions to clarify ideas

✓ listen politely

Extend and Assess

Focus on Science

Thinking Like a Scientist

Process Skill: Measuring

Answers for page 17: The book has the greatest mass; the lunch box has the least.

Answers for pages 26–27: 1. A stopwatch 2. Tennis ball and rock: four seconds. Leaf: 12 seconds. 3. The leaf is more affected by air resistance than the other objects because the leaf is shaped differently and has less mass. 4. Students may suggest that the shapes did affect how quickly the objects fell. The ball and rock are more streamlined than the leaf.

Check It Out: Answers will vary but students may suggest using another type of ball instead of the leaf.

▤ Measuring
Activity Master, Page 89

Students use the Activity Master to compare and draw conclusions about measurements.

Answers for page 89: 1. Measuring tape 2. The car on the dry road. 3. Students should suggest that there was less friction on the icy and wet roads than on the dry road, so the measurement was the shortest on the dry road. The greater the friction, the shorter the distance needed to stop. 4. People can learn that they need more time to stop on slick surfaces, so they should drive more carefully and more slowly.

Hands-on Science

Summary Students observe how different types of surfaces affect a moving object.

Tips Make sure stacks of books are the same height and the ruler is placed at the same angle each time.

Answers to Think *Gravity caused the marble to roll. Friction from the air and from the floor caused it to stop. The carpet caused greater friction than the smooth floor. The marble would roll farther on carpet because it is smoother than grass so there would be less friction.*

Assessment Options

Use the following assessment options to assess students' understanding.

Questions

Use the following questions during individual conferences or ask students to write the answers in their notebooks:

1 How does force cause an object to move?

2 What are Newton's three laws of motion? Provide one example that helps explain each.

3 What are two ways gravity affects objects either on Earth or in space? Why does this happen?

4 What is one way Galileo changed the way people think about force and motion?

5 How does a streamlined shape affect motion? Explain.

Assessment Activity

Students create a poster that illustrates and explains that forces used to set an object in motion. They can either draw the picture or use a picture from a magazine. They can then write captions using at least five of the words from the glossary.

Posters should

✓ use captions that include at least five words from the glossary
✓ use captions to explain action in the image
✓ use correct grammar and punctuation
✓ be well-organized and carefully prepared

Multiple-Choice Test

Use the multiple-choice test on page 115.

Cross-Curricular Connection

Mathematics

Have students research and compare gravity on Earth to gravity on other planets in our solar system. They can figure out whether their own body weight would be less or more on a given planet.

Home-School Connection

Students can discuss with family members the main ideas from *Using Force and Motion* and identify ways that Newton's three laws of motion can be applied in and around their home. For example, students and parents can discuss laws that can be applied to riding in a car or tossing a ball around in the yard.

Vocabulary: Use Context Clues

You can use context, the words and sentences that are around a word, to figure out the meaning of an unfamiliar word.

Read the sentences. Circle the words in each sentence that help you figure out the meaning of the word in italics. Write what you think the word means. Then look up the word in the glossary or a dictionary and see how closely its meaning matches the meaning you wrote from context.

1. Team A lost the tug-of-war game when Team B used more *force* to pull them down.

Meaning from context: _____

Meaning from glossary: _____

2. Did you know that, without Earth's *gravity,* you would float away from Earth?

Meaning from context: _____

Meaning from glossary: _____

3. The *friction* between my bike wheel and brakes caused my brake pad to wear down.

Meaning from context: _____

Meaning from glossary: _____

4. When I hit the baseball, *air resistance* slowed it down.

Meaning from context: _____

Meaning from glossary: _____

5. Please *measure* the sugar carefully for this recipe.

Meaning from context: _____

Meaning from glossary: _____

6. The shape of the racecar was *streamlined* to help it go faster.

Meaning from context: _____

Meaning from glossary: _____

Reading: Identify Cause-and-Effect Relationships

As you read *Using Force and Motion*, think about how forces affect the motion of objects. Then use what you learn to fill in the boxes with causes for each event.

What happens?   **Why does it happen?**

1. Objects start moving. ➡️

2. Objects fall to the ground when dropped. ➡️

3. Moving objects slow down and stop moving. ➡️

4. A racecar accelerates quickly. ➡️

5. A girl jumps on a diving board, and the diving board moves up and down. ➡️

6. Streamlined objects can move more quickly than other objects. ➡️

Reading Strategies

Writing: Prewrite

Write Steps in a Process

Choose a sport you'd like to write about. Then write five steps explaining how an athlete completes a move in that sport. For example, you might write steps explaining how a soccer player should set up and kick a goal. You might want to conduct research to learn more about the sport you choose.

When you have finished writing the five steps, you will explain how force and the laws of motion apply to each one.

The sport I choose: _____

The move or part of the sport I will focus on: _____

Step 1:

Forces and laws of motion:

Step 2:

Forces and laws of motion:

Step 3:

Forces and laws of motion:

Step 4:

Forces and laws of motion:

Step 5:

Forces and laws of motion:

Thinking Like a Scientist: Measuring

Read the information about cars and answer the questions that follow.

> Brakes help a car slow down when the car is in motion. When the brakes are applied, the car first slows down and then comes to a complete stop. How do road conditions affect the distance the car travels before it comes to a complete stop?

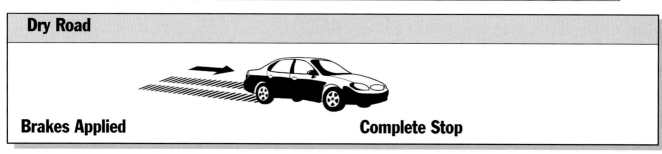

Dry Road

Brakes Applied　　　　　　　　　　　　**Complete Stop**

Wet Road

Brakes Applied　　　　　　　　　　　　**Complete Stop**

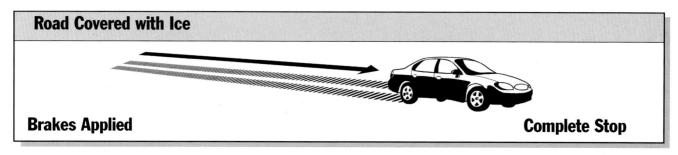

Road Covered with Ice

Brakes Applied　　　　　　　　　　　　**Complete Stop**

1. What tool would you use to measure distance on a road? _____

2. Which car traveled the farthest before it came to a complete stop? _____

3. How did friction affect each of the measurements? Explain. _____

4. How might these measurements be used to help people drive more safely? _____

Meeting Individual Needs

Teachers need to provide students with an education that prepares them to participate fully in the social, cultural, and economic life of the community and the country. Yet many challenges face today's classroom teachers. The student population reflects a wide diversity of cultures, languages, background experiences, learning styles, and ability levels. *Reading Expeditions* provides specific strategies that help teachers address the diverse needs of their students.

Gifted and Talented Students

Gifted and talented students are sometimes difficult to identify. These students can appear to be the most involved and creative, or they can be the most apathetic students in your classroom.

The strategies on the next page allow the classroom teacher to provide higher-level activities that benefit all students but that are particularly beneficial to gifted and talented students.

A gifted and talented student may exhibit any number of these qualities:

- Advanced cognitive ability and intellectual curiosity
- Dislike of drill and routine
- Creativity and sensitivity
- Strong motivation for self-selected projects and personal interests
- Gap between intellectual abilities and emotional, social, and physical maturity
- Unrealistic goals set either too high or too low
- Difficulty focusing attention and concentrating on finishing tasks
- Strong preference for individualized work, such as projects and independent study

When planning curriculum for gifted and talented students, keep in mind these guidelines:

- Involve students in planning, implementing, and evaluating learning tasks.
- Relate content to broad issues or themes.
- Structure work to allow for open-ended inquiry and project-based learning.
- Use outside resources, such as community members, businesses, and a variety of technologies.

Using *Reading Expeditions* with Gifted and Talented Students

Unless given unique and varied opportunities, gifted and talented students are often the ones who are most capable of learning but who will learn the least throughout a school year. It is important to assign gifted and talented students different assignments, not just more work. The academically talented student is often the one who is offered extra credit, which ultimately can mean more work and little learning for the student. Use these suggestions to adapt the teaching materials of *Reading Expeditions* for gifted and talented students.

Project-Based Learning

Involve the student in identifying projects based on the reading material—keeping choice and the student's interests as a basis for the projects. Projects may be short-term (lasting only a few days) or long-term (lasting several weeks). In designing longer projects, work with the student to outline a process that allows for checkpoints along the way. Help the student to articulate clearly what the end product will be as well as what he or she hopes to learn while doing the project.

Use the project ideas in the Writing and Research and in the Cross-Curricular Connection of the teaching notes for each book as springboards for generating ideas for book-level projects.

Involve Mentors

Invite members from the school or community to come into the classroom to work with students while they are involved in projects. These mentors can provide a different perspective on the learning tasks and offer different resources than typically available in the school setting.

Members of the science community would be especially valuable for projects related to books in the *Physical Science* series.

Use Contracts for Independent Study

Independent study is especially effective with some gifted and talented students. Write contracts for students so that they understand and agree to the criteria for independent study. If a student is not able to fulfill the agreement or contract, that student will be expected to return to working with the rest of the group.

Several features in *Reading Expeditions* would work well as the basis for independent study. For example, the Stay Tuned, Picture This, or Focus On features are excellent starting points. Students could also read all the books in the series to gain a broad overview of physical science concepts. Suggested resources in Science Notebook features are good introductions for students to research a science topic in greater depth.

Alternate Assessment Activities

Each lesson in the teaching notes suggests an alternate assessment activity for the book. These alternate activities can provide interesting and challenging tasks that tap into the talents of gifted students. Additional assessment ideas include: writing poetry, jingles or simple songs, a children's book, or a play; creating a newspaper or news broadcast, a brochure, maps or 3-D models, or an animated film or video; preparing a lesson to teach the class; developing a board or video game; producing a puppet show or play; and conducting an experiment.

Today's classrooms reflect the diverse and rich cultures of our country. Language minority students face many challenges as they acquire English while learning the core curriculum content. To adapt classroom instruction for the successful education of language minority students, there are several considerations to keep in mind.

English-language learners	To meet the needs of English-language learners, you can adapt instruction by
• Come to school with different levels of exposure to formal instruction in their native language • Bring different cultural backgrounds that will affect their own learning • Learn best when fully integrated into the school's general social and academic culture • Need to develop oral proficiency while concurrently beginning or transferring their literacy to the second language • Learn English best when it is taught through a content area	• Making instruction as comprehensible and relevant as possible • Creating a learning environment where ELL students are willing to contribute and take risks • Creating ample opportunities for ELL students to interact socially and academically with native-language speakers of English • Previewing literacy tasks with related oral language • Using only age-appropriate text that can be made comprehensible

Using *Reading Expeditions* With English-Language Learners

Reading Expeditions offers a rich selection of books that can be used to help build English-language proficiency for language minority students. This Teacher's Guide offers teaching notes for each book. The guidelines below can help you tailor the lesson to meet the needs of English-language learners.

Before Reading

Develop Vocabulary

Teach the content words that are highlighted in bold-faced type. Use these strategies to build content vocabulary.

▷ Teach the words in a meaningful context. Use the words in sentences in which the meaning and/or function of the word is important to understanding the sentence.

▷ Represent the words with visuals if possible. Use the illustrations and photographs in the book to develop understanding.

▷ Provide additional exposure to the words outside the lesson.

▷ Try to embed the words in the context of student speaking vocabulary before the words are used in literacy instruction.

▷ Maintain the same content-area standards for ELL students as for the general education population.

Activate Prior Knowledge

Use the suggested activities to tap into personal experiences and knowledge related to the book's content. Build on these connections so that students are well-grounded in the topics before reading. Use the graphic organizers suggested to make the content more tangible.

Build Background

Introduce the main ideas of the book through visuals, role-play, simulation, and hands-on activities prior to reading the book. Try a walk-through, using the illustrations to predict content.

During Reading

▷ Recognize that because students learning English have two cognitive tasks—understanding the concepts and interpreting the language—too much text impedes comprehension. Break text into manageable "chunks," using subheads as natural breaks.

▷ After reading each chunk of text, focus on the main ideas. State or write them clearly in complete sentences.

▷ Use graphic organizers to represent main ideas and related thought processes.

▷ Provide an audiocassette of the text, focus on the pictures, or use exemplary student summaries for those students who would benefit from alternate resources.

▷ Include English-language learners in instruction of higher-order thinking skills.

After Reading

▷ For **Responding,** organize discussion groups so that students fluent in English are working with English-language learners. Provide the questions included in **Responding** and allow groups to talk through the questions before initiating a class discussion.

▷ For the **Writing and Research** activity, prepare orally with methods such as an oral comparison and contrast, a retelling of a sequence, or an oral explanation of cause and effect.

▷ Provide modeling for the writing through class samples, paragraph frames, or sentence prompts that show key writing attributes, such as paragraph structure and transition words. Provide Word Banks and questions to answer.

▷ Have students pair up to share ideas orally prior to writing. ELL students can listen first and then say whatever they can, or they can listen twice.

▷ Provide alternative writing assignments for less proficient ELL students. They might tell/label/write about the photographs in the book, draw their understanding of ideas, tell or write using a graphic organizer, or use a Word Bank to fill in the omitted words in a summary.

▷ Write what the student is able to say and use the dictation as a reading source. Elaborate on the student's words by writing simple correct sentences, and read them to or with the student. Consider having a more proficient student, an aide, or a volunteer help with these adaptations.

Focus on Science

▷ Acknowledge that ELL students bring a wealth of experiences to the classroom that are valuable to all students.

▷ Recognize that students from other countries may be significantly more advanced or behind in content-area instruction received in their native countries.

▷ Use cooperative learning strategies and structures to increase student interaction.

▷ Validate the student's previous instruction through inclusion of diverse perspectives, world views, cultural bias, beliefs and values, and acknowledgment that there are cultural variations for performing common tasks. These variations can include writing structures and styles, mathematical procedures, systems of measurement, and content emphasis.

▷ Focus on the big ideas and the related thought processes.

Students with Special Needs

Students with special needs are typically unable to make satisfactory progress in the school without specific services and/or modifications made to the curriculum. Students with special needs have been diagnosed by either a medical evaluation or a team evaluation conducted at the school. These students may have more than one disability.

Some types of learning disabilities that may affect how a child learns include

- Attention (ADD, ADHD)
- Fine motor difficulties with such tasks as writing
- Speech and articulation difficulties
- Difficulty processing auditory directions and verbal commands
- Difficulty with word retrieval
- Difficulty organizing thoughts
- Emotional difficulties
- Sensory integration difficulties

Some useful classroom modifications for students with learning problems include

- Preferential seating
- Using clear simple language
- Never assuming the student understands the vocabulary and language of school
- Pairing a student with another for peer tutoring
- Using simple one-step directions
- Repeating directions
- Making directions visually accessible
- Using visual aids, such as photographs and concrete objects
- Relating materials to real-life experiences
- Clearly stating the lesson objectives and reviewing with students what they have learned
- Continual review of what was previously learned until it is established that the student has mastered the skill

Using *Reading Expeditions* with Students with Special Needs

Reading Expeditions offers rich content and reading for all students. Students with special needs can be read to or can read books based on interesting topics that contain age-appropriate vocabulary and develop comprehension.

This Teacher's Guide offers teaching notes for each book. The guidelines that follow can help you modify the lesson to reach all students, many of whom may have special needs.

Before Reading

The suggested strategies below are especially important for students with special needs. Use these to build on prior knowledge, preview the text, and develop content vocabulary.

▷ **Activate Prior Knowledge** Use the suggested activity to assess prior knowledge and to help students make connections between the text and personal experiences.

▷ **Preview and Set Purpose** Previewing, or overviewing, is a critical first step in reading. This involves looking at chapter titles, subheads, pictures and captions, and other visual clues to help identify the main ideas. Once main ideas are identified, help students generate questions so they will read to answer specific questions.

▷ **Vocabulary Strategy** Use the vocabulary strategy to develop content knowledge based on the key words.

During Reading

▷ **Read Strategically** This section helps to focus the reading of the text on finding specific information and using comprehension strategies to navigate through the text. The graphic organizers work as study guides for reading.

▷ **Model the Strategy Tip** to introduce students to the self-monitoring and self-correcting strategies used by good readers.

▷ Assign smaller chunks of text for reading, using subheads as natural breaks. Model a three-step process for students to use.

- Read the text.
- Ask yourself what it is about.
- Put the main ideas in your own words.

After Reading

Some students with special needs benefit from modified assignments.

▷ Pair students with a working buddy who can scribe for those students who have good verbal skills but have difficulty writing/organizing language and putting it down on paper.

▷ Limit the number and length of assignments.

▷ Allow students to draw illustrations, instead of writing, to assess comprehension.

Additional Ideas

Some students with special needs need more time to fully understand a concept or master a skill. They may need to "overlearn" a skill or concept to ensure that it can be applied and remembered. Plan frequent review and reinforcement of those core skills and concepts that have wide application.

Students with special needs benefit from working with peer tutors. Explain to students the role of a tutor and tutee and then pair students so that they take turns in these roles.

Overview of Titles

Focus on Nonfiction		Focus on Science
Title	**Genre and Text Features**	**Science Learning Objectives**
Acids and Bases	• Expository text • Chapter titles and subheads • Photographs and illustrations • Charts, diagrams, and sidebars • Captions and labels • Table of contents, glossary, and index	• Explain how substances are placed in categories according to their characteristics • Identify properties of acids and bases • Describe the harmful effects of acids and bases • Describe methods of identifying acids and bases • Identify common acids and bases
Chemical Changes	• Expository text • Photographs and captions • Diagrams, illustrations, and sidebars • Chapter titles and subheads • Table of contents, glossary, and index	• Distinguish between physical and chemical changes • Understand that chemical reactions involve changes in energy • Identify factors that affect reaction rate • Explain the role of enzymes in chemical reactions • Describe the importance of chemical reactions in daily life
Introduction to Energy	• Expository text • Chapter titles and subheads • Photographs and captions • Sidebars • Table of contents, glossary, and index	• Describe the relationship between energy and work • Explain the difference between energy of motion and stored energy • Identify situations in which energy is transferred • Describe different forms of energy • Explain how heat is related to motion
Machines Make It Move	• Expository text • Photographs and captions • Sidebars • Diagrams and time line • Chapter titles and subheads • Contents, glossary, and index	• Identify the six simple machines • Explain how people build machines to solve certain problems • Explain how ancient engineers used simple machines in their work • Explain how the position and motion of objects can be changed by pushing or pulling • Relate the size of change in position and motion to the strength of the push or pull
Matter, Matter Everywhere	• Expository text • Photographs and captions • Sidebars • Diagrams, charts, and time line • Chapter titles and subheads • Contents, glossary, and index	• Explain how properties are used to classify and describe matter • Identify tools used to measure properties • Explain how matter can exist in different states: solid, liquid, gas, and plasma • Compare chemical changes to physical changes in matter • Describe how the periodic table organizes elements • Recognize that atoms make up all living and nonliving things • Differentiate elements and compounds • Identify scientists who have contributed to the field of chemistry

Physical Science Series

Communication Skills

Reading Skills	Writing Skills	Listening, Speaking, and Viewing
Skill Focus • Compare and contrast • Use context clues Supporting Skills • Summarize • Draw conclusions • Identify cause-and-effect relationships • Make judgments	Writing Focus • Write steps in a process (expository) Supporting Skills • Prewrite • Conduct research • Record knowledge	• Give an oral presentation
Skill Focus • Draw conclusions • Determine word knowledge Supporting Skills • Summarize • Compare and contrast • Reread	Writing Focus • Write steps in a process (expository) Supporting Skills • Prewrite • Conduct research • Record knowledge	• Give an oral presentation
Skill Focus • Identify cause-and-effect relationships • Use specialized words Supporting Skills • Summarize • Make judgments • Compare and contrast • Draw conclusions	Writing Focus • Write a letter (persuasive) Supporting Skills • Use the writing process • Write for different purposes • Respond to others' writing	• Give an oral presentation
Skill Focus • Draw conclusions • Use context clues Supporting Skills • Identify main idea and details • Compare and contrast • Use images to aid comprehension	Writing Focus • Write directions (expository) • Prewrite Supporting Skills • Write for a specific audience • Conduct research	• Give an oral presentation
Skill Focus • Identify main idea and details • Relate words Supporting Skills • Compare and contrast • Summarize • Self-question	Writing Focus • Write a report (expository) • Prewrite Supporting Skills • Use an outline • Conduct research	• Analyze an image

Focus on Nonfiction		Focus on Science
Title	**Genre and Text Features**	**Science Learning Objectives**
Newton's Laws	• Expository text • Photographs and captions • Sidebars • Chapter titles and subheads • Contents, glossary, and index	• Explain Newton's first, second, and third laws of motion • Give examples of how Newton's laws of motion explain the movements of everyday objects • Identify some of Galileo's and Newton's characteristics that helped them in their scientific work • Describe some of Newton's scientific discoveries and accomplishments
The Magic of Light and Sound	• Expository text • Photographs and captions • Sidebars • Diagrams • Chapter titles and subheads • Contents, glossary, and index	• Explain how light waves and sound waves travel • Describe the difference between reflection and refraction of light • Learn how people see light and hear sounds • Understand that both light and sound waves can reflect off objects • Recognize that sound waves travel through different materials at different speeds but cannot travel through a vacuum • Recognize how light and sound technologies are used in scientific investigations and in daily life
The Mystery of Magnets	• Expository text • Chapter titles and subheads • Photographs and captions • Diagrams and illustrations • Sidebars and features • Table of contents, glossary, and index	• Describe how magnets act on objects and other magnets • Explain how Earth is a magnet • Identify discoveries that people have made throughout history about magnetism • Explore the relationship between electricity and magnetism • Understand how people continue to use magnets to solve problems
Understanding Electricity	• Expository text • Photographs and captions • Sidebars • Illustrations and diagrams • Chapter titles and subheads • Contents, glossary, and index	• Define and give examples of energy • Describe an electric circuit and its parts • Recognize that electric circuits can produce light, heat, and magnetic effects • Define blackouts and explain how people can avoid them • Recognize that many scientists have contributed to our understanding of electricity • Identify various resources used for creating electricity
Using Force and Motion	• Expository text • Photographs and captions • Sidebars • Diagrams and charts • Chapter titles and subheads • Contents, glossary, and index	• Explain how the position of an object can be changed by pushing or pulling • Identify gravity as a force that affects objects on Earth, keeps Earth in orbit around the sun, and keeps the moon, satellites, and other objects in orbit around Earth • Identify and explain Newton's laws of motion • Explain how magnets can be used to move objects • Recognize that many scientists have contributed to our understanding of force and motion

Physical Science Series

Communication Skills

Reading Skills	Writing Skills	Listening, Speaking, and Viewing
Skill Focus • Identify cause-and-effect relationships • Use specialized words **Supporting Skills** • Identify main ideas and details • Summarize	**Writing Focus** • Write an introduction (descriptive) **Supporting Skills** • Use the writing process • Create an outline • Respond to others' writing	• Present an introduction
Skill Focus • Draw conclusions • Use prefixes **Supporting Skills** • Recognize cause-and-effect relationships • Compare and contrast • Reread	**Writing Focus** • Write a report (expository) **Supporting Skills** • Use the writing process • Use an outline • Conduct research	• Create a diagram
Skill Focus • Identify main ideas and details • Relate words **Supporting Skills** • Make generalizations • Summarize • Identify cause-and-effect relationships	**Writing Focus** • Write a report (expository) **Supporting Skills** • Use the writing process • Use an outline • Conduct research	• Give an oral presentation
Skill Focus • Make generalizations • Use specialized words **Supporting Skills** • Identify cause-and-effect relationships • Summarize • Use graphic organizers	**Writing Focus** • Write a speech (persuasive) • Use the writing process **Supporting Skills** • Write for a specific audience • Conduct research	• Give an oral presentation
Skill Focus • Recognize cause-and-effect relationships • Use context clues **Supporting Skills** • Summarize • Identify main idea and details • Paraphrase	**Writing Focus** • Write steps in a process (expository) **Supporting Skills** • Prewrite • Conduct research	• Give an oral presentation

Correlation to National Standards

National Science Education Standards

STANDARDS: GRADES K–4

I. SCIENCE AS INQUIRY
   Abilities necessary to do scientific inquiry
   Understanding about scientific inquiry

II. PHYSICAL SCIENCE
   Properties of objects and materials
   Position and motion of objects
   Light, heat, electricity, and magnetism

III. LIFE SCIENCE
   Characteristics of organisms
   Life cycles of organisms
   Organisms and environments

IV. EARTH AND SPACE SCIENCE
   Properties of Earth materials
   Objects in the sky
   Changes in the Earth and sky

V. SCIENCE AND TECHNOLOGY
   Abilities of technological design
   Understanding about science and technology
   Abilities to distinguish between natural objects
      and objects made by humans

VI. SCIENCE IN PERSONAL AND
   SOCIAL PERSPECTIVES
   Personal health
   Characteristics and changes in populations
   Types of resources
   Changes in environments
   Science and technology in local challenges

VII. HISTORY AND NATURE OF
   SCIENCE
   Science as a human endeavor

STANDARDS: GRADES 5–8

I. SCIENCE AS INQUIRY
   Abilities necessary to do scientific inquiry
   Understanding about scientific inquiry

II. PHYSICAL SCIENCE
   Properties of matter and changes in matter
   Motions and forces
   Transfer of energy

III. LIFE SCIENCE
   Structure and function in living systems
   Reproduction and heredity
   Regulation and behavior
   Populations and ecosystems
   Diversity and adaptations of organisms

IV. EARTH AND SPACE SCIENCE
   Structure of the Earth system
   Earth's history
   Earth in the solar system

V. SCIENCE AND TECHNOLOGY
   Abilities of technological design
   Understanding about science and technology

VI. SCIENCE IN PERSONAL AND
   SOCIAL PERSPECTIVES
   Personal health
   Populations, resources, and environments
   Natural hazards
   Risks and benefits
   Science and technology in society

VII. HISTORY AND NATURE OF
   SCIENCE
   Science as a human endeavor
   Nature of science
   History of science

Correlation to National Science Education Standards

Science Content Standards: K–4

	Acids and Bases	Chemical Changes	Introduction to Energy	Machines make It Move	Matter, Matter Everywhere	Newton's Laws	The Magic of Light and Sound	The Mystery of Magnets	Understanding Electricity	Using Force and Motion
Science as Inquiry	✓	✓		✓	✓	✓	✓	✓	✓	✓
Physical Science										
Properties of objects and materials	✓	✓		✓			✓			
Position and motion of objects*				✓		✓			✓	
Light, heat, electricity, and magnetism			✓				✓	✓	✓	✓
Life Science										
Characteristics of organisms										
Life cycles of organisms										
Organisms and environments										
Earth and Space Science										
Properties of Earth materials										
Objects in the sky										
Changes in Earth and sky										
Science and Technology		✓	✓	✓	✓	✓	✓	✓	✓	✓
Science in Personal and Social Perspectives	✓						✓	✓		
History and Nature of Science		✓		✓	✓	✓	✓	✓	✓	✓

Science Content Standards: 5–8

	Acids and Bases	Chemical Changes	Introduction to Energy	Machines make It Move	Matter, Matter Everywhere	Newton's Laws	The Magic of Light and Sound	The Mystery of Magnets	Understanding Electricity	Using Force and Motion
Science as Inquiry	✓	✓		✓	✓	✓	✓	✓	✓	✓
Physical Science										
Properties of matter and changes in matter	✓	✓			✓					
Motions and forces			✓	✓		✓				✓
Transfer of energy			✓	✓		✓	✓		✓	✓
Life Science										
Structure and function in living systems										
Reproduction and heredity										
Regulation and behavior										
Populations and ecosystems										
Diversity and adaptations of organisms										
Earth and Space Science										
Structure of the Earth system										
Earth's history										
Earth in the solar system										✓
Science and Technology		✓	✓	✓	✓	✓	✓	✓	✓	✓
Science in Personal and Social Perspectives	✓									
History and Nature of Science		✓		✓	✓	✓	✓	✓	✓	✓

Literacy Internet Resources

Visit the *Reading Expeditions* Website

www.nationalgeographic.com/education/readingexpeds

Reading Expeditions has its own place on the National Geographic Education website. Explore the online resources that support and extend this series. This site provides a variety of options to support your instruction, including teaching materials for specific titles, information on readability levels, and correlations to national standards.

- **Comprehensive Teaching Notes and Activity Masters**

  The downloadable lesson notes for each title include a variety of teaching strategies. Additionally, for each title, you'll find printable blackline masters that develop literacy and content skills.

- **Correlation to National Standards**

  With national standards posted online, you'll be able to view how each title correlates to the science and language arts standards. *Reading Expeditions* has been developed using national standards from the National Science Education Standards.

- **Information on Readabilities**

  The online chart will help you compare the series with frequently used leveling systems such as the Lexile framework and the Fry readability formula.

- **Assessment Materials**

  The online assessment materials will include a variety of tools for measuring students' developmental progress.

Keep checking the *Reading Expeditions* site for more new resources and for updates about additional titles to come.

Just log onto **www.nationalgeographic.com/ education/readingexpeds** and see how *Reading Expeditions* continues to grow.

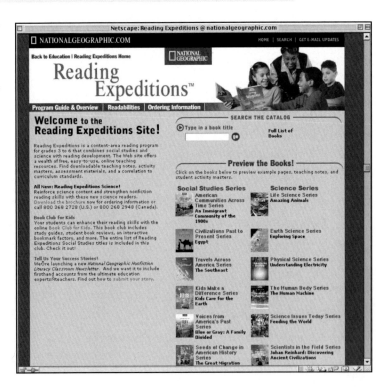

Online Resources to Extend Literacy Learning

A number of excellent websites from educational organizations and government agencies provide helpful Internet resources. The following sites may assist you in preparation for your lessons.

International Reading Association (IRA)

http://www.reading.org

As stated on their website, the mission of the IRA is to "promote high levels of literacy for all." The website provides a wealth of reading research materials, conference information, and articles from journals and other publications.

Reading Online

http://www.readingonline.org

This site, published by the International Reading Association, is an electronic journal for K–12 literacy educators.

Reading Is Fundamental (RIF)

http://www.rif.org

Reading Is Fundamental, Inc. (RIF), a national grassroots organization, serves young people in varied settings, including schools, community centers, and Boys and Girls Clubs. The RIF website includes information about their programs, literacy activities for children, parents, and volunteers, and literacy links for educators.

U.S. Department of Education

http://www.ed.gov

This website, offers an ever growing collection of information about the Department, including the latest news about educational programs, policies and legislation, grant opportunities, publications, and research and statistics. The site also includes special collections of information for parents, teachers, and students.

National Institute for Literacy (NIFL)

http://www.nifl.gov

NIFL is an independent federal organization working toward the goal of having a fully literate America in the 21st century. In addition to information about programs, services, policy, and legislation, the NIFL site also offers a feature called LINCS. LINCS provides access to literacy-related information such as state and national policies and classroom practices. It also allows all users to join electronic discussion forums.

Reading Matters

http://www.nea.org/readingmatters

This site is part of the National Education Association's (NEA) website, and it offers year-round news, expert advice, classroom and home activities, reading strategies for informational texts, and resources for adults to help children improve their reading skills.

Educational Resources Information Center (ERIC)

http://www.indiana.edu/~eric_rec/

ERIC is a national information system designed to provide ready access to an extensive body of education-related literature. The database offers the world's largest source of education information, providing a variety of services and products.

Assessment Overview

Although one purpose of assessment is to measure performance so that results can be shared with parents and school administrators, the primary purpose of assessment is to gather information to inform instruction. Assessment offers valuable insights into students' learning and allows teachers to plan instruction that supports and challenges students. It deals with both the knowledge students attain and the process of learning. A variety of assessment tools are available with *Reading Expeditions*.

Discussion Questions

For each title in *Reading Expeditions*, a series of discussion questions are provided in the Teacher's Guide (See **Assessment Options: Questions**). These questions tap into students' understanding of the information in the text and invite students to use the text to make connections, draw conclusions, and make generalizations. The questions can be used in individual reading conferences, or students can write responses in their reading notebooks. In evaluating student responses, you may want to use the following rubric.

Questions

Use the following questions during individual conferences or ask students to write the answers in their notebooks:

1 What is one example of each state of matter?
2 Explain the difference between a chemical change and a physical change. Provide an example of each.
3 What are some properties of gold?
4 Are most of the things in the world made up of compounds? Explain.
5 Why is a hypothesis important to an experiment?

Teacher's Guide page 45 for *Matter, Matter Everywhere*

Rubric for Evaluating Responses

4	Answer addresses all parts of the question and shows sound reasoning, with appropriate examples drawn from the text to support conclusions and inferences.
3	Answer addresses most parts of the question and shows inferential thinking in filling in unstated connections. There may be some omissions or minor errors of fact.
2	Answer does not deal directly with the question but may deal with some related aspect of the question. The response reflects a literal understanding of the text but shows little inferential comprehension of the information in the text.
1	Answer shows little comprehension of the question or the text. It may be unrelated or inappropriate.

Multiple-Choice Tests

A multiple-choice test is offered for each title in *Reading Expeditions*. The physical science tests appear on pages 106–115 of this handbook. The comprehension and vocabulary tests offer a quick assessment of basic understandings of the text. Questions in the test cover the key ideas and concept words presented in the title and provide students with practice in taking multiple-choice tests. The answer key for each test is provided on page 116.

Assessment Activity

For each title in *Reading Expeditions*, there is an Assessment Activity provided in the teaching notes (See **Assessment Options: Assessment Activity**). This activity outlines an alternative performance-based assessment option in which students can make a product or give a performance that demonstrates an understanding of the text. This alternative assessment can provide insight into how well the student understands and applies the knowledge learned from the text.

For each Assessment Activity, an evaluation checklist is provided to help measure performance against defined criteria. These checklists typically address both the content and the execution of the assessment product. Clearly defined criteria make it easier to give an objective evaluation of the activity. In addition, you may want to record anecdotal notes that give insight into such skills as problem solving and collaboration skills.

Performance-based assessments are especially useful with students for whom paper-and-pencil activities do not reflect the student's learning. These activities can tap into special skills that are often overlooked by traditional assessment tools.

Assessment Activity

Ask students to create a diagram that shows the relationship between matter, compounds, and elements. Students should include labels and captions to communicate their ideas. Students can use *Matter, Matter Everywhere* and other resources to complete their diagrams.

Teacher's Guide page 45 for
Matter, Matter Everywhere

Name _____

Acids and Bases

Circle the letter of the correct answer.

1. Which of the following is tested by a universal indicator?

   a. pH

   b. smell

   c. taste

   d. color

2. Which of the following is a property of acids?

   a. tastes sour

   b. corrodes metal

   c. has a pH less than 7

   d. all of the above

3. Which of the following can be harmful to many living things?

   a. acetic acids in pickle jars

   b. acid rain

   c. acid in lemons

   d. bases used for cooking

4. What is one way to safely identify acids and bases?

   a. tasting an unknown substance

   b. smelling an unknown substance

   c. using litmus paper

   d. none of the above

5. Which of the following is true of a base?

   a. It turns litmus paper red.

   b. It turns a universal indicator bright red or pink.

   c. It tastes sour.

   d. It turns litmus paper blue.

Complete each sentence by writing the correct word or term from the Word Box.

base	predict	fossil fuels	pH	indicator	ions

6. Litmus paper is used as a(n) _____ for acids and bases.

7. The _____ scale tells the strength of acids and bases.

8. Acids release hydrogen _____ when they are mixed with water.

9. Scientists _____ when they make an educated guess based on experience.

10. Burning _____ can cause acid rain.

Name _____

Chemical Changes

Circle the letter of the correct answer.

1. Which of the following is a type of catalyst?

  a. a hydrogen fuel cell

  b. an enzyme

  c. an endotherm

  d. an ion

2. The speed at which a chemical reaction takes place is called its

  a. exotherm.

  b. catalyst.

  c. physical change.

  d. reaction rate.

3. Which term describes a chemical reaction that releases energy?

  a. exothermic

  b. endothermic

  c. ionic

  d. molecular

4. Carbon and oxygen can combine to form carbon dioxide. What is the product in this chemical reaction?

  a. carbon

  b. oxygen

  c. carbon dioxide

  d. dioxide

5. Which of the following is NOT an example of a chemical change?

  a. plastic broken into small pieces

  b. oxygen and hydrogen combine to form water

  c. a nail becomes rusted

  d. sparks come off of a sparkler

Write the letter of the correct definition next to each word.

_____ **6.** catalyst

_____ **7.** reactant

_____ **8.** product

_____ **9.** atom

_____ **10.** reaction rate

a. starting substance in a chemical reaction

b. the smallest part of an element

c. the substance resulting from a chemical reaction

d. a substance that makes a chemical reaction occur more easily

e. the speed of a chemical reaction

Name _____

Introduction to Energy

Circle the letter of the correct answer.

1. Energy and work are related because

  a. work makes energy change form.

  b. energy is the ability to do work.

  c. energy keeps work from happening.

  d. work creates energy.

2. Examples of stored energy include all of the following EXCEPT

  a. gasoline that makes a car move.

  b. the food you eat so that you can be active.

  c. a galloping horse.

  d. a rubber band that makes a toy airplane fly.

3. What type of energy travels through power lines?

  a. sound energy

  b. light energy

  c. electrical energy

  d. chemical energy

4. All of the following are examples of a transfer of energy EXCEPT

  a. a bowling ball hitting the pins.

  b. wearing warm clothes when it is cold.

  c. ice melting.

  d. a log burning on a campfire.

5. Insulation is important because

  a. it can keep people and animals from getting too cold.

  b. it can keep food hot.

  c. it can keep a house cool in the summer and warm in the winter.

  d. all of the above

Complete each sentence by writing the correct word or term from the Word Box.

chemical energy	stored energy	transfer	measure	work	insulation

6. A rock sitting at the edge of a cliff has _____.

7. Energy can _____ from one object to another.

8. Material that reduces the transfer of heat is _____.

9. Moving an object results in _____ being done.

10. Fuels such as food and gasoline store _____.

Name _____

Machines Make It Move

Circle the letter of the correct answer.

1. Simples machines were used for all of the following ancient accomplishments EXCEPT

   a. two-wheeled chariots.

   b. the Great Pyramid.

   c. the great moai.

   d. bicycles.

2. Simple machines include all of the following EXCEPT

   a. screw.

   b. pulley.

   c. engine.

   d. wedge.

3. Levers are often used to

   a. lift things more easily.

   b. make pottery.

   c. hold things together.

   d. hold a wheel to a bike.

4. Machines are used

   a. at work.

   b. for play.

   c. at home.

   d. all of the above

5. Scientists control variables in experiments in order to

   a. to see what happens if all parts of the experiment change.

   b. to help them test just one variable at a time.

   c. to make work easier.

   d. to do an experiment faster.

Complete each sentence by writing the correct word or term from the Word Box.

compound machine	fulcrum	axle	inclined plane	archaeologist	gear

6. A(n) _____ can be found at the center of a seesaw.

7. A(n) _____ is made up of many simple machines.

8. A wheel with teeth on the outside is called a(n) _____ .

9. A(n) _____ supports a wheel and helps the wheel turn.

10. Do you know which _____ studied the ancient Egyptian pyramids?

Multiple-Choice Test

Matter, Matter Everywhere

Circle the letter of the correct answer.

1. States of matter include all of the following EXCEPT

   a. density.

   b. gas.

   c. liquid.

   d. solid.

2. You would use Archimedes' Principle to measure

   a. boiling liquids.

   b. invisible gases.

   c. oddly shaped solids.

   d. plasma.

3. An element is

   a. a substance made up of only one kind of atom.

   b. made when two types of atoms join together.

   c. made from different types of atoms.

   d. classified today as either fire, water, air, or earth.

4. A chemical change in matter

   a. happens when ice melts.

   b. means the arrangement of atoms has changed and a new substance is formed.

   c. means a substance changes state.

   d. happens when water freezes.

5. All of the following are always important to conducting experiments EXCEPT

   a. using a ruler.

   b. communicating results.

   c. writing a hypothesis.

   d. writing clear steps.

Write the letter of the correct word next to each definition.

_____ 6. the smallest unit of matter that has the characteristics of an element

_____ 7. a measure of how much space an object takes up

_____ 8. a state of matter that doesn't have a definite shape or volume

_____ 9. a measure of how much matter is in a substance

_____ 10. a form or condition of matter

a. mass

b. gas

c. atom

d. volume

e. state

Multiple-Choice Test

Newton's Laws

Circle the letter of the correct answer.

1. Isaac Newton developed laws of

   a. motion.

   b. sound.

   c. time.

   d. heredity.

2. Newton's second law of motion states that force is related to

   a. distance.

   b. action and reaction.

   c. mass and acceleration.

   d. friction.

3. Which of the following is an example of an invention that uses Newton's laws of motion?

   a. an airplane

   b. a roller coaster

   c. a windmill

   d. all of the above

4. Which of the following is NOT related to one of Newton's laws of motion?

   a. force

   b. light

   c. inertia

   d. friction

5. You experience one of Newton's laws of motion when you do which of the following?

   a. ride a bicycle

   b. throw a ball

   c. walk up the stairs

   d. all of the above

Complete each sentence by writing the correct word or term from the Word Box.

mass	inertia	friction	force	circular motion	acceleration

6. The tendency of an object to resist change is _____.

7. A push and a pull are each a(n) _____.

8. The amount of matter something has is its _____.

9. The change in an object's speed or direction over time is _____.

10. A force that resists motion when two objects rub against each other is _____.

The Magic of Light and Sound

Circle the letter of the correct answer.

1. Both light and sound are forms of energy that travel in

   a. vibrations.

   b. outer space.

   c. prisms.

   d. waves.

2. Sound echoes when it reflects off a surface, much like light when it

   a. reflects off a mirror.

   b. is produced from a flashlight.

   c. refracts through a lens.

   d. refracts through a prism.

3. Sir Isaac Newton

   a. used echoes to measure the speed of sound.

   b. invented the telescope.

   c. developed sonar.

   d. all of the above

4. Light waves can do all of the following EXCEPT

   a. reflect.

   b. bend around objects.

   c. refract.

   d. be absorbed.

5. All of the following inventions use light EXCEPT

   a. fiber optic cable.

   b. laser.

   c. microscope.

   d. sonar.

Write the letter of the correct definition next to each word.

_____ **6.** bioluminescence   **a.** frequencies that are lower than people can hear

_____ **7.** infrasound   **b.** bounce back

_____ **8.** reflect   **c.** frequencies that are higher than people can hear

_____ **9.** refraction   **d.** light produced by living things

_____ **10.** ultrasound   **e.** bending of light as it passes from one substance to another

Name _____

The Mystery of Magnets

Circle the letter of the correct answer.

1. A magnet is used in all of the following
EXCEPT

   a. when someone uses scissors to cut paper.

   b. when someone plays music on a tape.

   c. when a compass points north.

   d. when a doctor scans a person's brain with an
MRI device.

2. Hans Christian Oersted discovered that

   a. the northern lights are caused by magnetism.

   b. magnets have north and south poles.

   c. magnets respond to electricity.

   d. magnetite is magnetic.

3. All of the following are places magnetism
occurs in nature EXCEPT

   a. the North and South Poles of Earth.

   b. in a rock called magnetite.

   c. in the northern lights.

   d. in an incomplete electrical circuit.

4. Which of the following is true about
magnets?

   a. North poles attract north poles.

   b. South poles attract south poles.

   c. North poles attract south poles.

   d. all of the above

5. For an electromagnet to work, it must
have all of the following EXCEPT

   a. electricity and magnetism.

   b. a compass pointing north.

   c. a coil of wire with magnetic material
inside it.

   d. electricity flowing in a complete
circuit.

Write the letter of the correct definition next to each word or term.

_____ **6.** attract

_____ **7.** compass

_____ **8.** magnetic field

_____ **9.** pole

_____ **10.** repel

   a. a tool with a magnetic needle that lines up north-south

   b. to pull

   c. the area of a magnet where magnetism is strongest

   d. to push away

   e. the region of force that exists around a magnet

Name _____

Understanding Electricity

Circle the letter of the correct answer.

1. The parts of an atom that make electric power possible are called

   a. volts.

   b. static.

   c. electrons.

   d. generators.

2. Electric circuits can produce all of the following EXCEPT

   a. light.

   b. rainbows.

   c. heat.

   d. magnetism.

3. Lewis Latimer

   a. wrote the first textbook on electrical power and lighting systems.

   b. invented the first light bulb.

   c. discovered current electricity.

   d. built the first electric generator.

4. All of the following can be used to produce electricity EXCEPT

   a. the sun.

   b. the wind.

   c. an insulator.

   d. fossil fuels.

5. Scientists build models for all of the following reasons EXCEPT

   a. to test ideas.

   b. to learn how something works.

   c. to replace something.

   d. to help explain a topic to others.

Complete each sentence by writing the correct word from the Word Box.

switch	volt	static	circuit	insulator	generator

6. The _____ is a unit of electrical pressure.

7. A(n) _____ uses a magnet to produce current electricity.

8. Electrons can flow through a looped path called a(n) _____ .

9. A(n) _____ is a material that stops or slows the flow of electrons.

10. With _____ electricity, electrons move in one large discharge.

Name _____

Multiple-Choice Test

Using Force and Motion

Circle the letter of the correct answer.

1. A force can be all of the following EXCEPT

　　a. a slippery thin layer between moving parts.

　　b. a push or pull on an object.

　　c. something that makes an object stop.

　　d. something that makes an object change direction.

2. Isaac Newton built upon the ideas of

　　a. Elijah McCoy.

　　b. Galileo Galilei.

　　c. astronauts who study space and gravity.

　　d. none of the above

3. A girl diving from a diving board is an example of Newton's third law of motion, which says that

　　a. objects that are streamlined can travel more quickly.

　　b. an object doesn't change its state of motion unless it's forced to.

　　c. for every action, there is an equal and opposite reaction.

　　d. gravity keeps the moon in orbit around Earth.

4. To make something accelerate more quickly, you would

　　a. apply less force.

　　b. apply more force.

　　c. use greater air resistance.

　　d. none of the above

5. Tools used for measuring include all of the following EXCEPT

　　a. stopwatch.

　　b. brakes.

　　c. ruler.

　　d. scale.

Write the letter of the correct definition next to each word.

_____ **6.** gravity

_____ **7.** friction

_____ **8.** air resistance

_____ **9.** measure

_____ **10.** streamlined

a. a force that resists motion when two objects rub together

b. to find certain amounts

c. a force that pulls any two objects together

d. having a smooth shape that reduces air resistance

e. friction caused by air

Acids and Bases

1. a   6. indicator
2. d   7. pH
3. b   8. ions
4. c   9. predict
5. d   10. fossil fuels

Chemical Changes

1. b   6. d
2. d   7. a
3. a   8. c
4. c   9. b
5. a   10. e

Introduction to Energy

1. b   6. stored energy
2. c   7. transfer
3. c   8. insulation
4. b   9. work
5. d   10. chemical energy

Machines Make It Move

1. d   6. fulcrum
2. c   7. compound
                  machine
3. a   8. gear
4. d   9. axle
5. b   10. archaeologist

Matter, Matter Everywhere

1. a   6. c
2. c   7. d
3. a   8. b
4. b   9. a
5. a   10. e

Newton's Laws

1. a   6. inertia
2. c   7. force
3. d   8. mass
4. b   9. acceleration
5. d   10. friction

The Magic of Light and Sound

1. d   6. d
2. a   7. a
3. a   8. b
4. b   9. e
5. d   10. c

The Mystery of Magnets

1. a   6. b
2. c   7. a
3. d   8. e
4. c   9. c
5. b   10. d

Understanding Electricity

1. c   6. volt
2. b   7. generator
3. a   8. circuit
4. c   9. insulator
5. c   10. static

Using Force and Motion

1. a   6. c
2. b   7. a
3. c   8. e
4. b   9. b
5. b   10. d

Using Portfolios and Retellings

Reading Conferences

Individual reading conferences provide an opportunity for teachers and students to assess and evaluate an individual's progress and to set goals. This is an opportunity for teachers to talk with students about their reading—what books they have read, what difficulties they might be having, what they enjoyed, what they learned or found interesting in their reading, and what goals they want to set.

While the conference may appear to be an informal discussion, the most effective conferences follow a predictable structure that the teacher and the student prepare for. Students and teachers know how to prepare for the conference, what they will talk about during the conference, and what they will do after the conference. To help students prepare for the conference, you may want to copy and distribute the checklist on page 118 or one that matches your plan for reading conferences.

Reading Portfolios

The reading portfolio is a key element of the conference. This working folder includes a variety of materials: lists of books read, writing done in response to reading, self-evaluation lists in which the student notes those things that are going well, and a list of goals for reading.

Some teachers find it helpful to have individuals keep a reading record. This is an ongoing accounting in which the student records daily reading and reflections on that reading. Each day the student records the pages read and makes notes of things to discuss in the reading conference. Many teachers find these valuable tools to learn about the student as a reader. You may wish to copy and distribute the reading record on page 119.

Retellings

Retellings can be a valuable part of the reading conference. They offer a tool for assessing a student's comprehension of an informational piece.

An unaided retelling is done by asking the student to tell you everything he or she remembers about the book. You may tell the student to assume that you have not read the book and he or she is to tell you everything about it.

An aided retelling is done by asking questions that you have prepared in advance. These may prompt the student to tell about the most important ideas, how the student reacted to the book, and whether the student can relate the book to any personal experience. See the checklist on page 120 to help evaluate retellings.

Name _____ Date _____

How to Prepare for My Reading Conference

☐ Update my reading folder

☐ Update my reading record

☐ Be ready to retell what I have read

☐ Update my list of goals

☐ Be ready to talk about things I found interesting

☐ Be ready to talk about things I learned

☐ Be ready to talk about any parts that I found hard

Notes:

_____

_____

_____

_____

_____

Name _____ Date _____

Reading Record

Date	Author and Title	Pages Read	Notes for Reading Conference

NATIONAL GEOGRAPHIC

READING EXPEDITIONS®

Name _____ Date _____

Title _____ Author _____

Checklist for Evaluating Retellings

The Retelling was

☐ unaided   ☐ aided

Main Ideas

☐ All the main ideas were included.

☐ Most of the main ideas were included.

☐ Some of the main ideas were included.

Supporting Details

☐ Supporting details were included and logically related to the main ideas.

☐ Supporting details were included but not related to the main ideas.

☐ Few supporting details were included.

Use of Reading Strategies

☐ Photographs and illustrations were used in understanding text.

☐ Reader made valid inferences.

☐ Reader drew logical conclusions.

☐ Reader asked important questions.

Additional Observations

_____

_____

_____

Using Graphic Organizers

Graphic organizers are visual representations of information. They can be used to help assess students' understanding of informational text as well as their ability to communicate information in different ways. Graphic organizers are important because they help students to comprehend, summarize, and synthesize complex ideas and information.

The books in the *Reading Expeditions Physical Science* series cover a wide variety of scientific topics. Graphic organizers are excellent tools to help examine these fundamental science concepts as students reconstruct and process the information presented in the text.

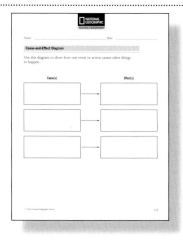

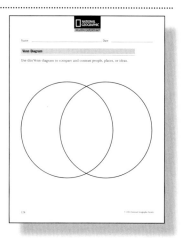

Cause-and-Effect Diagram
(Page 123)

Cause-and-effect diagrams show causal relationships among actions and events. They can show how one or more actions or events affects subsequent events. Understanding cause and effect helps students to understand that scientific study involves analyzing the factors that cause changes in the natural world. By studying causes and effects, students also can gain insight into the interactions of matter and energy on Earth.

A cause-and-effect diagram can be used with each of the *Physical Science* titles in *Reading Expeditions*. Have students select an action or event and then trace the results or effects of this action. You may want students to create several cause-and-effect diagrams for some titles.

Venn Diagram
(Page 124)

A Venn diagram is especially useful with text that compares and contrasts information. It allows students to work with two concepts or sets of information and identify what is common and what is different.

While a Venn diagram can be used with many titles in *Reading Expeditions*, it is especially suited to *Acids and Bases, Matter, Matter Everywhere, The Magic of Light and Sound, Chemical Changes,* and *Machines Make It Move.* These books are structured to compare and contrast various physical science concepts—from physical and chemical changes, to states of matter, to similarities and differences among simple machines.

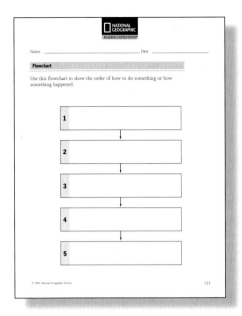

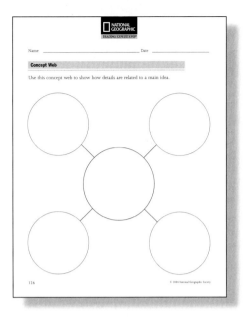

Flowchart
(Page 125)

The flowchart is an effective tool to represent a sequence of events. This graphic can show the order of particular events as well as the steps in a process for procedural text.

While the flowchart can be used with many titles in *Reading Expeditions*, it is especially suited to *Understanding Electricity, Introduction to Energy, Newton's Laws, The Mystery of Magnets, Using Force and Motion,* and *The Magic of Light and Sound.* You may wish to adjust the number of steps in the flowchart to fit specific topics in each title.

Concept Web
(Page 126)

A concept web is a useful visual for showing a variety of relationships. Concept webs can show hierarchical relationships and are well suited to show main idea and details.

A concept web can be used with each *Physical Science* title in *Reading Expeditions.* Work with students to select topics within the book and then ask them to use the concept web to represent important ideas and relationships. Concept webs often show one main circle with several secondary circles as spokes off the center. You may wish to add secondary circles to the concept web provided on page 79 to reflect the content of specific titles.

Name _____ Date _____

Cause-and-Effect Diagram

Use this diagram to show how one event or action causes other things to happen.

Cause(s)   **Effect(s)**

Name _____ Date _____

Venn Diagram

Use this Venn diagram to compare and contrast people, places, or ideas.

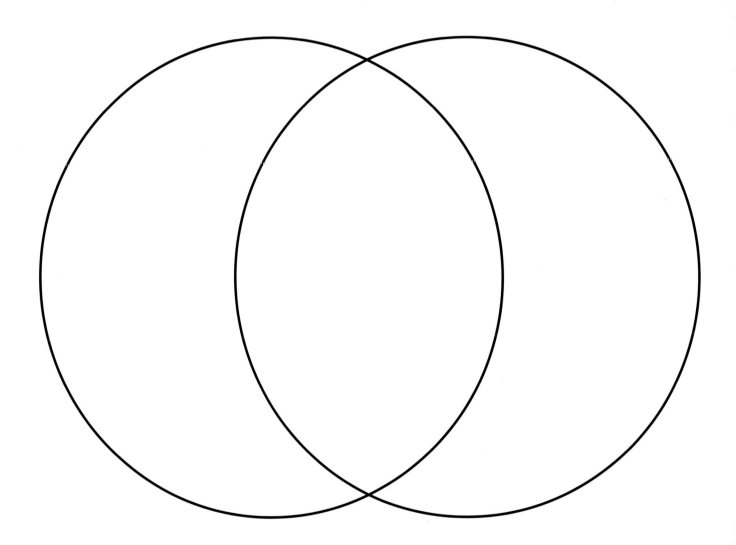

Name _____ Date _____

Flowchart

Use this flowchart to show the order of how to do something or how something happened.

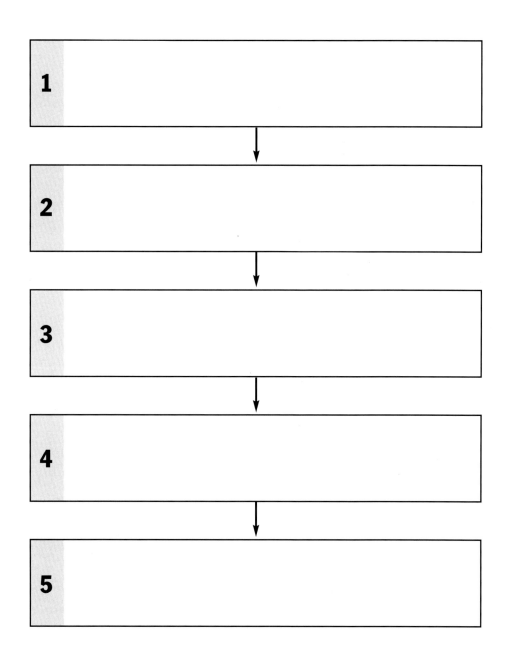

Name _____ Date _____

Concept Web

Use this concept web to show how details are related to a main idea.

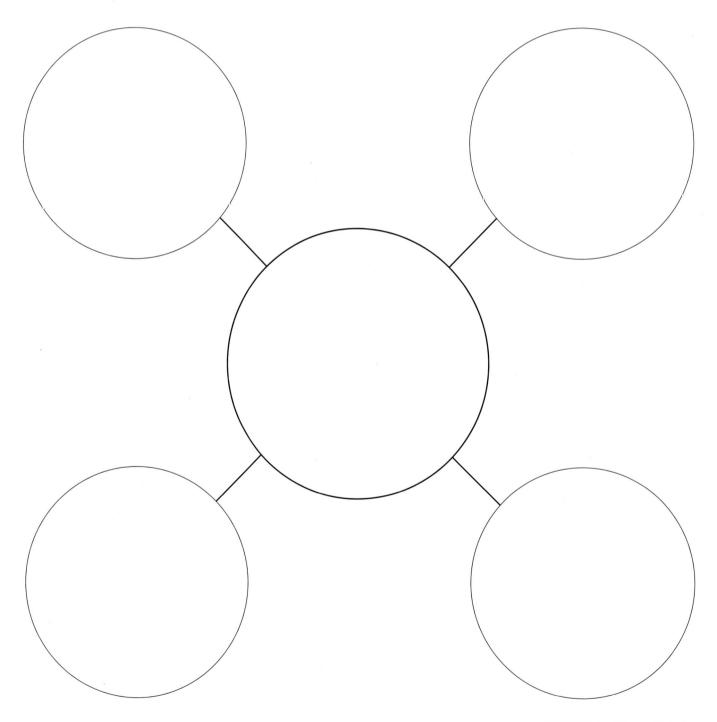

Index

Notes